Aeroplane Affair

Aeroplane Affair

AN AERONAUTICAL AUTOBIOGRAPHY

JOHN O. ISAACS

AIR
RESEARCH
·PUBLICATIONS·

AIR RESEARCH PUBLICATIONS
34 Elm Road, New Malden, Surrey KT3 3HD,
Great Britain

ISBN 1 871187 05 2

© 1988 John O. Isaacs

Typeset by Qualitext, Salisbury SP2 7BE
and printed by LR Printing Services Ltd,
Crawley, West Sussex RH10 2QN

Dedicated to
The memory of my parents.
They don't make them like that any more.

CONTENTS

ACKNOWLEDGEMENTS

My thanks are due to all whose paths have touched mine, those who are named herein, the many more who are not and all of whom unwittingly provided the experience for this memoir; to those who counselled and kindled its execution including Barry Thompson, New Zealand Fury pilot; Hugh Scanlan, pilot and writer; Bob Cole, RAF test pilot, John Barber, USAAF Black Widow pilot; to Mrs June East (née Slingsby) who painstakingly typed the manuscript; to Vivian Bellamy who . . . well his influence will become apparent to all who peruse the following pages.

FOREWORD

by

AIR COMMODORE CHRISTOPHER PAUL, CB, DFC, FRAeS
(Former President of the Popular Flying Association)

For a number of years, it has been my privilege to be one of the Judges at the annual Popular Flying Association Rally; each year John Isaacs' designs have been among the prize winners, and few have given more delight than that small beauty, the Isaacs Fury.

I had not realised until John invited me to write this foreword how often and closely our paths had crossed before we actually met. When he began work with Supermarine at Woolston, I was frequently there, generally to collect a Walrus for Lee-on-Solent; but sometimes because there was a magic about the people and about the birthplace of the Supermarine Schneider Trophy seaplanes, and, finally, the Spitfire. But, for me, an astonishing coincidence, if it was that, was to find that the birthplace of the Isaacs Fury was none other than the house of Doctor Urmston of Botley, the same house from which John Urmston's predecessor had attended the birth of both my sons.

In this book, John reveals himself not only as the dedicated aeroplane enthusiast, but also as a writer whose descriptions of Hampshire in his youth are a delight; and furthermore as a gifted artist, illustrating his own text. My favourite shows the old Itchen chain ferry on its crossing towards Woolston, with the Supermarine works in the background. John was there when they were destroyed by German bombs, and was lucky, as he describes, to escape alive. But he stayed with Supermarine and was with the Spitfire from its birth to the end of its production. Clearly the magic stuck, and later, resulted in the Isaacs 'mini-Spit' which, demonstrated by former Boscombe Down test pilot Bob Cole, enthralled airshow spectators over many years.

John Isaacs describes his Spitfire's design, building problems, and completion at some length, including his triumphant visit with it to Oshkosh. He is too modest about his own achievements; but, reading between the lines, it is clear that he is an able and experienced pilot; this comes out in the hilarious, and absorbing account of his time at Eastleigh when the exuberant Vivian Bellamy presided over the postwar revival of the old Hampshire Aeroplane Club.

I am sure, however, that John's favourite aeroplane ever since he watched 43 Squadron flying them at Tangmere, has been the Hawker Fury.

It was my own great good fortune to be accepted into the Royal Air Force when squadrons were just beginning to re-equip with aircraft and engines significantly better than those of 1919.

There arrived a breed of Rolls-Royce Kestrel-engined biplanes, unsurpassed in their generation. Prominent among these were the Hawker Fury fighter; and its later deck-landing cousin, the Nimrod. These two, between them, gave me some of the most wonderful open-cockpit flying that it has been my good fortune to experience. No need, therefore, for me to exaggerate the sheer delight of the Isaacs Fury. And I now know what enjoyment it gives, all over the world, as John relates, for example, in his visit to New Zealand.

Naturally, a good deal of this book is devoted to the design and construction of the Isaacs Fury; fitting what is essentially a new design into the scaled-down envelope of the full-size original. It is an absorbing account of planning and persistence, to overcome problems galore before final triumph. But the climax is John's account of helping to design and build the full-sized, Kestrel-engined Fury replica. Here is revealed John the detective, questing worldwide for original drawings and, with hope almost gone, discovering an original Kestrel on the other side of the world. Then John the designer, reconstructing missing drawings, delving with apparent delight into the complications of three-dimensional trigonometry caused by biplane wings of unequal span, stagger, raked interplane struts, finding the correct length of lift and landing wires, all to be specially ordered; an account peppered with humour and telling us of bedrooms full of aeroplane; about those cajoled and charmed into helping and lending specialist skills. And, as all through his book, generous credit given to others.

John's book has been, to me, something of a revelation. I have long been convinced that the truly great aircraft designers were much more than aircraft engineers. One has only to look at the Spitfire, Roy Chadwick's Lancaster, Mario Castoldi's superb Macchi Schneider Trophy Seaplanes, and, my own favourite, the de Havilland Mosquito, to understand that their creators were artists whose vision inspired their work.

So too with John Isaacs. With these qualities he is generously endowed; and with more, including a determined persistence without which the Kestrel Fury could never have been built and flown.

How I wish I could become a 'born-again' pilot, young enough to experience once more the delights of the Kestrel-engined Fury! I am perfectly sure, however, that John's Furies, great and small, will continue to delight us all for a long time to come. And if his book inspires future artist-designers to follow in his footsteps, what a great master to follow!

GJCP
February, 1986.

PREFACE

By happy chance the wise old aviator had driven up from his lair in Cornwall and accepted a suggestion that he fly with me. 'Good, what are you going to teach me today?' I said. 'I can't teach you anything,' he replied, quite erroneously, 'I'll just sit in the back and enjoy the ride.'

By mutual consent we waited, curiously, to watch a visiting two-seat microlight take-off first. In the stiffish breeze it climbed strongly from the grass strip before the ear-piercing scream of its two-stroke ceased abruptly when the tiny engine seized: in silence it flopped into the overshoot just short of a wood. Thoughtfully, I taxied out for take off, then, as the Chipmunk headed west, at 300 feet I raised the flaps and glanced across the widening view of the valley at the slumbering village with its clock-towered church opposite the 'Greyhound': at 800 feet I eased the throttle but still allowed the aeroplane to drift gently upwards. To starboard, the vast runway at Boscombe Down swam into view; to port, Pepperbox Hill dominated the railway line. It was a June day in January 1982 – clear, bright, sunny but with interesting little tufts of scattered woolly cloud: in short it was Air Marshal's weather.

Soon the three groups of hangars hove into view at Old Sarum where I once watched Atlas and Hector biplanes picking up messages from a line stretched between two poles. Over Salisbury's cathedral we turned north to trace the outline of the old airfield at High Post. At 4,000 feet, I set the throttle to an 80 knot level cruise as we purred past timeless Stonehenge. Behind me, the voice pointed out Bulford Church which he claimed to have watched grow to alarming proportions as he hurtled vertically towards it in a Harvard with extended undercarriage and, the voice continued, 'There is the hill where old 'so and so' crashed in a Hurricane in 1940. Sometimes,' he ruminated, 'I can't believe that it happened, it all seems so long ago.'

When the twisting Avon led us to Netheravon, I kept a sharp lookout for parachutists. Ahead lay historic Upavon, the little town of Pewsey, and white horses cut into the hillsides but a gentle sweep to starboard, on to a south-easterly heading, carried us towards the lush green triangle of disused Andover airfield. 'I see no Sidestrands', I said. Three miles to its west, racetrack-ringed Thruxton sprawled in the afternoon sun, its once famous black hangar now reduced to a green-roofed store while aeroplanes decayed in the open. Turning south we flew between the grassy expanse of Middle Wallop, whence Spitfires had soared, and the derelict runways of Chilbolton, scene of a shared scare; and so back to the airstrip on the ridge, its stately line of trees now decimated by the Dutch disease. Still there was magic in the air so I headed towards a comfortable cottonwool cloud, circled it, playfully prodded it with a wingtip and only then descended, applied hot air, turned crosswind, lowered flaps at 65 knots, trimmed back to 60 knots, slipped over the hedge, eased back the stick until G-AOUP's wheels kissed, thankful that, with the w.o.a. in the back, it was a 'greaser'.

But let me start at the beginning.

John O. Isaacs
Chandlers Ford, December 1985

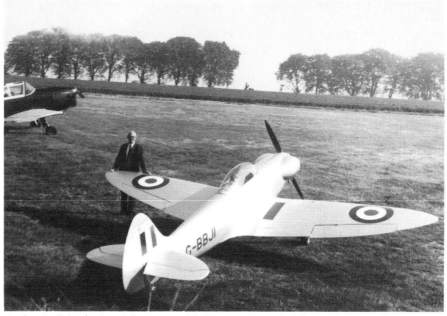

Author in Faireyland – John Isaacs with Chipmunk and Spitfire, 1975 – see Chapter 11.

CHAPTER 1

SCHOOLBOY (1920–1937)

I was born lucky for I had, that most precious of life's gifts, two good parents who inculcated in me a sense of discipline. My father was born in 1888 as one of a large family: he lost his father, a blacksmith journeyman, at an early age due, it was said, to a heart attack brought on by excitement at a political victory of his favoured (Liberal) candidate. As his mother was unable to support the whole family, my father and one of his brothers had to live in an orphanage until, at 13, he went to work as messenger-boy with the White Star Line Shipping Company, an occupation which sometimes sent him shyly into a smoke-filled bar at Southampton's grand South Western Hotel to seek out a wanted official.

A keen sportsman all his life, he became Secretary of the Southampton Wheelers and would cycle for miles over dust-choked, unpaved roads to take part in a race meeting before pedalling home again at night. For a while, he ran a belt-driven Rudge motorcycle, which vehicular experience was to exempt him from the obligatory driving test when he bought his first car in the mid 1930s. In an age when amusements were self-made and correspondence courses flourished, he showed a fair hand at pencil drawing and took a memory-training course of Pelmanism. He was in training camp with the Territorial Army at Lulworth Cove when war broke out in 1914: to release the Regulars for duty in France they were quickly sent to India, he as a Vickers machine-gun instructor. In August 1916, his name appeared in Battalion Orders issued at Secunderabad when he was promoted to Company Sergeant-Major 'C' Company of the 2/5th Bn., Hampshire Regiment. He was later commissioned as 2nd Lt. Eventually, back in England, sickness kept him for some time in the military hospital at Netley which presumably spared him the horrors of the Western Front.

Whereas my father was a wisely shrewd man of emphatic views, my mother was a gentle, cheery woman also of high integrity: she never complained and would suffer fools much more gladly although she ruled her three children firmly. I never knew her father, first an ordnance office draughtsman – then a general outfitter, but grandmother, who was not always in good health, lived with us until she died in 1928 while I was still a junior schoolboy: in her eyes I could do no wrong. Before the war my mother had been a schoolteacher with an annual stipend of fifty pounds, cycling many a mile to teach classes of well over fifty and, she claimed, 'they all learnt something'.

Of my own early life, a kaleidoscope of flickering images remains etched in memory. Visits to my father's old home, across the Itchen toll bridge at Northam, up to the very top of Bitterne Hill where hung the 3 in 1 picture to entrance a child: stand in front of it to see a tall ship in full sail, but move to left or right and two quite different images magically appeared. Being taken for walks: walks along Hill Lane, straw spread on the road outside a house of sickness to muffle the clip-clop of horses' hooves: walks on the Common; lakes where swans jostled with model yachts: walks through the cemetery to wonder at the engine carved on a headstone: walks to the Marlands where a showman dived into a water tank ablaze with flame: walks to play on a waterlapped beach near the station. Christmas; sleeping on the floor in the attic as uncles and aunts arrived: spare leaves in the great table for mother to feed sixteen from the turkey cooked in the kitchen range: threepenny bits in the pudding: the magic lantern show.

On my first day at Miss Cotton's Western District Infants School, my parents were taken-aback to find that the teachers had placed me alongside the local rabbi's son: they had done their best but names do not register religion. I enjoyed an aptitude for drawing with pastel crayons and, although no child prodigy, I won a prize for perseverance.

In the town centre, street traders hawked their wares in the gathering winter dusk from naphtha-lit barrows. Outside Edwin Jones' store, after a tiring day mum would say to us children, 'Shall we walk home instead of going by tram and spend the fare at Allen's in Commercial Road to buy sweets?' A favourite treat on special occasions was tea at the Cadena with rich, cream-oozing chocolate japs. Saturday mornings frequently meant free film shows for children or lantern slide lectures by missionary explorers who had actually been to such far-flung places as Labrador or Africa. When we grew bigger, the family regularly visited the swimming baths where dad taught us to swim: how eagerly we hurried to the little shop on the Western Esplanade to buy our penn'orth of broken biscuits to eat on the walk home.

At home we sat with earphones clamped over our heads, each joined by wire to a special board at which dad tinkered while he talked of catswhiskers until, unbelievably, we could hear someone talking in London. Some years later, I was taken to a building in the Portland Street area to see a moving picture of a lady on a screen. Descending the stairs dad then led me across the road into another building where, in front of lights, sat the same lady in person: it seemed a miracle.

I liked to read, draw and paint and, in that age of steam, although ships delighted me and I loved locomotives, gradually, subtly, the aeroplane began to distract me.

In 1929, from the vantage point of a stony beach whither I had been transported in the dicky seat of an uncle's Bull-nose Morris, I glimpsed the fleeting minuscule shapes of scarlet and silver-blue seaplanes darting like dragonflies over the waters of the Solent where those exquisite masterpieces of Mario Castoldi and Reginald Mitchell fought out with high drama their recurrent technical battle for the Schneider Trophy and national prestige. Fifty years after, it was to be my privilege to wrest those close-kept Italian secrets from the past when, enthralled, I pored over prints of the Macchi seaplane design drawings which gave a rare insight into the artistic mind of the portly Dr Castoldi.

In 1930, the year after the Supermarine S6's win for Britain at Cowes, I was granted a ringside seat for a contest of a different kind when the annual King's Cup Air Race was flown over a 750 mile circuit in a single day, starting and finishing at Hanworth, near London. The first turning point, for the largest entry ever attracted, was at Hamble after which the 88 competing aeroplanes flew north-west to a compulsory halt at Whitchurch (Bristol), a leg which led them straight over Southampton. As the first machine left Hanworth at 7.00 am and the whole field was dispatched over a period of nearly four hours, a stream of various types passed low over the family home for a large part of that morning in July. The big, old, three-storey semi-detached, with its eleven rooms, tended to block the overall view of the sky, so I spent an exciting morning rushing from the front garden to the back to gaze as long as possible at each of the variegated aeroplanes glinting in the sunshine as they dashed low over the quiet town. Intensely impressive among all the light aeroplanes was the big twin-engined Vickers Vellore biplane flying as scratch machine. After more than seven hours full-throttle flying, the race was won by Miss Winifred Brown in a Cirrus-engined Avian.

In contrast to such rapture came that Sunday morning in October when the family walked home from church, subdued, digesting the news, as a stunned nation tried to come to terms with the shock of the unbelievable tragedy to the R101.

The following year, beneath a lowering August sky, I stood on the

'Island Queen', the Spartan 3-seater, G-ABAZ at Shanklin.

muddied, crowd-flattened meadows of Atlantic Park which linked the Swaythling district of Southampton to neighbouring Eastleigh. Between me and the London and South Western railway line lay the wooden-trussed arc-roofed hangars vacated by the US Navy in 1919; later the area had become a transit camp for European immigrants to the USA, hence the Park's name.

The itinerant air circus had come to town; it consisted of Captain C. D. Barnard's sturdy Fokker monoplane, a Cierva C19 autogiro and a Spartan three-seat biplane with John Tranum as parachutist. I tightly gripped the furled umbrella left in my care by my father who joined the little group of joyriders climbing aboard the boxlike monoplane with its high thick wing. On the fuselage behind the uncowled 500 hp Jupiter engine was painted *The Spider*. I was not to appreciate the dual significance of that symbol of perseverance for many years; not until I learned the history of that famous Fokker F.VIIA and came to know myself and fulfil my boyhood dreams.

In those less affluent times, summer holidays were traditionally spent at nearby seaside resorts. Thus was one introduced to the peaceful delights of family-board in a Sandown bungalow an hour's paddle-steamer voyage and a short train journey distant, passing golden days of childhood on like-toned beaches until taken one memorable day to a grass field near Shanklin. Here, ensconsed, as if with Victorian caution, back to the engine and facing a stranger I sat in the elongated open front cockpit of the Spartan 3 seater G-ABAZ, peering in wonder over the high coaming at the receding sweep of Sandown Bay as we made a brief foray over sparkling blue sea. An uncle's camera clicked, encapturing *Island Queen*, mistress of my baptême de l'air.

Then, subsequent to the ordeal of a daylong scholarship examination sat on the premises of the deadly rival, Tauntons, I found myself happily installed at Southampton's prestigious King Edward VI School where I also joined the Scout troop run with dedication by Messrs. Berry and Arnold. Never a willing 'muddied oaf' nor with ear attuned to the crack of willow on leather, my escape finally came by way of the school Rowing Club. Moreover, the rumour that the master in charge, 'Tich' Langdon, had been a wartime kite balloon observer at once increased his stature in my eyes. Contentedly, we pulled our 'tub-fours' up the half mile of river from Woodmill to Mansbridge, slipped carefully through its narrow arch to turn

We pulled our 'tub-fours' up the river . . . (J.O.I. at bow).

our craft in the wider waters lapping the gardens of the 'White Swan' on the very threshold of the Municipal Airport.

Southampton nestles in the fork of the rivers Test and Itchen which converge into Southampton Water with the diamond jewel of the Isle of Wight to seaward; it had long been established as a hub of ocean trade. Since my father worked for the White Star Line, he was able to produce occasional boarding passes which enriched the romance and glamour of the huge liners with their 'tween decks smoking rooms, restaurants, gymnasiums, swimming baths and ornately appointed cabins, giving no hint that in a few decades they would be gone forever, ousted by the aeroplane. Yet the immediate area bore ample evidence of the tyro aviation for the rolling downs of Hampshire and its southern seaboard figure prominently in its early history; air stations were established at Southampton, Hamble, Lee-on-the-Solent, Gosport, Worthy Down, Andover, at least as early as 1918. Further, in 1913, that eccentric pioneer, Noel Pemberton-Billing, established an aircraft company on a disused coal wharf at Woolston on the east bank of the Itchen. He coined the name Supermarine since he intended to specialize in machines which would fly over the sea.

As Woolston's most direct tenuous links with Southampton consisted of a pair of cable-guided ferry boats, they gave, in passage, a changing view of Supermarine's sprawl of corrugated-iron-clad sheds which spread along the river front screening Hazel Road. While crossing, to visit family friends in Woolston, a Southampton flying-boat could often be seen bobbing at its moorings as the clumsy floating bridge passed close by the factory. The rambling old house in Woolston bore its treasury of books; shelves groaned beneath the weight of successive years of *Jane's Fighting Ships* and some of the first aircraft annuals for, in his youth, the master of the household, Will Biggs, had meticulously drawn the silhouettes and uniform scale plans for those early volumes. *All the World's Airships (Aeroplanes and Dirigibles)* founded and edited by Fred T. Jane, second year of issue 1910–11, was a priceless gift to receive from this gentle draughtsman.

Sometimes, for a fine summer day's outing, the family would ride in a tramcar or walk the two miles to the floating-bridge, cross the river, bus four miles to Bursledon on the Hamble, cross the bridge, bus a further four miles to be deposited in the quiet little village of Titchfield on the Meon. From here, that modest stream meandered through two miles of water meadows offering a shady stroll until, emerging from the trees near Titchfield Haven on to a shingle beach, the promised land was spread before us in all its breathtaking glory, the sparkling Solent.

Huddled together on the beach were perhaps thirty wooden dwellings one of which my father would rent for the family annual holiday. And oh, how we kids loved Meon! The primitive hut with its dim oil-lamp lighting and its creosote-tainted bucket loo was a palace to us. Tender young feet learnt to cope with the shingle as we swam daily and in a rowing boat we would pull out from the shore, lining up two landmarks to fix our bearings before casting anchor and steeling ourselves to bait hooks with wriggling lugworms dug from the sea's edge and haul in the whiting-pout that mother would cook over a primus stove.

Hamble aerodrome, home of Air Service Training Ltd, lay unseen round the headland four miles to the northwest; three miles westward across the water the squat castle pinpointed Calshot Spit with its RAF flying-boat base; four miles south, across the Solent, Cowes on the Medina marked the top corner of the diamond Isle of Wight from whence emanated spectacular flurries of yachts and fireworks during the annual Cowes Week. At intervals, majestic ocean liners glided into view before slipping silently away to the New World or the Old and sometimes I thrilled to a pulse-quickening grey silhouette of the Senior Service. Southeast of our haven, where the tall needle tower of Lee-on-the-Solent then rose from the flat shore line, lay the two-mile distant air station with its clutch of seaplanes, while beyond, Portsmouth's ancient guardian forts slumbered in the shimmering sea haze.

Following the coast towards Hamble a cliff-edge path, no more than thirty feet above the beach, led for a mile to a valleyed inlet known as Brownwich Farm, scene of illicit woodland feasts on 'found' farm eggs and youthful experiments with Woodbines. But to me that cliff top walk was sheer heaven for among the golden crops was an untilled grass field used for practice landings by the silver-winged black Avro Cadet biplanes from AST. The sound of their engines sent the blood coursing through my veins with excitement as I hurried from the hut to that practice meadow to be as near as possible to the aeroplanes. Sometimes the pilots would wave to my sisters and me and dive to clifftop level as they followed the coast back to base; I little dreamt I would be able to emulate such delights fifteen years later. Out

'. . . visits to Service air stations at Gosport . . .' (a Blackburn Shark).

on the Solent, the stately Southampton flying-boats of 201 Squadron from Calshot practised alightings and one memorable day, a Saro Cloud amphibian dropped on to the water close to our beach for the crew to swim.

East of our holiday home the coastal road led past the catch of small sailing craft in the Haven, up the slope to Hill Head village, round the undulating curves of a small promontory to arrive at the long straight promenade of Lee. Here, traffic would come to a halt when Fairey IIIF float-planes were trundled across the main road from the Naval Air Station hangars and launched into the Solent by waist-deep handlers. Continuing for a mile or two, beyond the Browndown rifle range, brought a cyclist to Fort Grange, the Gosport airfield enshrined as the temple of Lt Colonel Smith-Barry's revolutionary flying school in the First World War; here could be found the wheeled aircraft of the Fleet Air Arm, home from the sea, Baffins and Sharks, in company with RAF Vildebeests.

Back at home, too, the bicycle was the key to the kingdom. Hamble was only a short ride from Southampton and it was possible to enter the edge of the airfield where the Shell railway line crossed the main road to separate the flying field from the hangars. I would stay contentedly all day near the parked Avro biplanes and, if lucky, sometimes a Siskin, Atlas, Cutty Sark or even a three-engined Avro Five. A dramatic heterogeneous formation of these school aeroplanes would occasionally fly over Southampton. One day Mollison's famous trans-Atlantic Dragon, *Seafarer*, under new ownership and renamed *Trail of the Caribou*, crashed on the edge of the aerodrome. I read of this in the newspaper next day and, pedalling furiously to Hamble, picked up as a souvenir a discarded, black-painted, fabric tear-off patch.

A ride beyond Winchester to Worthy Down revealed the dark forms of ancient, lumbering Virginia bombers in their Nivo green finish and, their less conventional, replacement Handley Page Heyfords, with high slender fuselages attached directly to the upper wings and enormous wheel spats hanging like talons from the strut-suspended lower wings. The longest ride was to Andover where, from the A303, the fabulous aerobatic twin-engined Sidestrand day bombers of 101 Squadron could be seen drawn up in front of the hangars on that lush green triangular airfield.

Naturally the most frequent ride was to local Atlantic Park, granted an air of respectability in 1932 when Southampton Corporation re-opened it as a municipal aerodrome. Our favourite haunt was a spur off Wide Lane, near the Supermarine hangar, which gave an unimpeded view across the field. Here, enchanted, we gazed upon the big Vickers biplane bomber with its four engines in tandem pairs; the royally colourful Viastra monoplane built for the Prince of Wales; Airspeed Couriers with their novel retracting wheels; three-engined, trousered Spartan Cruisers from the Isle of Wight; and Dragons and DH.86s departing for the sandy low-tide beaches of St.

Schoolboy with Avro Tutor at Hamble 1935.

The aviation scene in the 1930s . . an Airspeed Courier.

Aubin's Bay for there was then no airfield in Jersey.

But when the circus came to town, summoned by the morning's mass formation arrival flight, we marched boldly through the main entrance paying our shilling admission fee. Sir Alan Cobham, who had done much to initiate the building of municipal aerodromes, launched the first of his National Aviation Day tours in April 1932. Around his hired Handley Page W10 giant airliner, he assembled two specially built Airspeed Ferries, four Avro 504Ks, a DH.60 Moth, a Tiger Moth, a Southern Martlet, a C19 autogiro and a two-seat glider.

The display programme included a grand parade of all the aircraft in formation carrying fare-paying passengers, aerobatics, crazy flying, pylon racing, parachute descents, balloon bursting, comic flour bag bombing and the hair-raising wing walking activities of Martin Hearn who I saw sitting on the wheel of a looping 504. The 'upside down' aces ('six times a day, seven days a week') were Charles Turner Hughes and Geoffrey Tyson who also

Comper Swift belonging to the Prince of Wales (G-ABWW), and a Wicko, built on the aerodrome, at Southampton.

21

The family home in Landguard Road, Southampton, about 1930.

snatched a handkerchief from the ground with a wingtip. I did not then fully appreciate the staggering size of this barnstorming operation for they gave performances at a different town each day throughout the season.

At Southampton, in 1934, the Hampshire Aeroplane Club promoted a festival of flying which brought a visit from No. 1 Squadron's Tangmere-based prestigious Hawker Fury fighters. The incomparable splendour of a full squadron of those immaculate silver biplanes, with twin red bar insignia, taxying over the green sward while their highly buffed cowlings glinted in the summer sunshine was to haunt me for a lifetime. Oh truly 'In Omnibus Princeps'!

That same year brought a domestic crisis which must have worried my parents acutely when, under pressure from the government of the day, the two giants, Cunard and White Star, were merged with the eventual disappearance of the latter's name. Fortunately my father retained his job and later rose to become head of his department. Perhaps it was the greater sense of security that led him to buy his first car the next year; it was a one year old Morris Saloon which cost £100. As soon as I was old enough, he taught me to drive and lent the car for me to visit Empire Air Day displays at Tangmere and Old Sarum. And, on the ground, my sporting heroes were men of speed on wheels for the Bentley Boys such as Tim Birkin, Woolf Barnato, Dr Benjafield and Sammy Davis were names to be reckoned with. Besides, had not the great W.O. developed rotary engines for the Sopwith Camel before winning more lasting fame with his big battleship-like cars at Le Mans, successes which goaded Ettore Bugatti to dub them 'the fastest lorries on the road?''

In 1935, that French pioneer of home-built aircraft, Henri Mignet, demonstrated his ill-fated Pou-du-Ciel at Southampton and in the wake of the Flying Flea craze which swept the country I went to see a locally-built example at the back of Owen's fish and chip shop in Shirley. Once, returning on the paddle-steamer from the Isle of Wight, I was entranced as we passed Calshot, to find the huge six-engined Short Sarafand flying boat swinging at her moorings; I stared and stared until the dusk haze swallowed her. Another time, at a house belonging to a friend's aunt, we were idly launching simple gliders from an upstairs room when our curiosity was aroused by an unusual engine noise. Astounded at what we saw, we rushed down on to the street to get a better view of that most incredible monster cruising immediately above us, gleaming silver, gigantic, red bar and Swastika on the tail, awe-inspiring, 803 feet long with a 424 foot girth; it was the Zeppelin *Hindenburg*.

But if the sights, sounds and smells of flying had spun their alluring web then the might of the pen was to complete the ensnarement for I was early enmeshed in the enchantment of aviation lore. Schoolboy pocket money would sometimes buy a copy of Stanley Spooner's weekly *Flight* or the outspoken C. G. Grey's *Aeroplane* wherein we could enthuse over technicalities of the latest stylish biplanes. Also, in the spring of 1932, during the worst depression this country had ever known, a new magazine appeared called *Popular Flying*; it cost sixpence each month throughout its seven and a half years existence and it brought a whole new world. I read that its forthright editor, Captain W. E. Johns, had flown DH.4s with No. 55 Squadron as part of Trenchard's Independent Air Force attacking Rhine targets until he was shot down over Germany shortly before the Armistice.

DH 86A at Eastleigh.

His intention was to present in interesting form a faithful picture of all aspects of aviation. Convinced of the absolute inevitability of the Second World War, from the beginning, he did his best to goad the authorities into adequate preparation by advocating a strong Royal Air Force. He became unpopular in official quarters though he should have received a decoration for, in recording the exploits and brilliant achievements of Mannock, Ball and countless others who set a standard for tradition, he stimulated and inspired the generation who had to fight that war; the politicians eventually had him removed from office.

Early issues carried entertaining tales of a Camel pilot by William Earle, soon disclosed as the editor; thus was Biggles born. The list of contributors embraced constructors and pilots, the famous such as Mermoz or the infamous such as Goering. Later I was to fly with some of the authors including Stewart Keith Jopp who received severe injuries in the first war

The elegant Spartan Cruiser with trousered undercarriage.

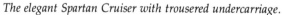

yet served as a ferry pilot in the second. Among the profusion of subjects covered, the frail fabric-clad biplanes of 1914–18 fostered in me a life-long interest; their distinctive shapes and characteristics dominated early modelling and drawing activities. When I was promised a day in London as a special treat, my earnest desire to visit the Imperial War Museum, which had on display a real Sopwith Camel and an R.E.8, must have saddened my ex-soldier father; but Culley's famous steed seemed to epitomize the designer's art in that first dreadful conflict. The popular Biggles tales gave it fictional prominence though the grim realities of the day were emphasised in V. M. Yeates' brilliant novel *Winged Victory*. In it he wrote of the aeroplane: 'A Camel hated an inexperienced hand and flopped into a frantic spin at the least opportunity. They were unlike ordinary aeroplanes, being quite unstable, immoderately tail heavy, so light on the controls that the slightest jerk or inaccuracy would hurl them all over the sky, difficult to land, deadly to crash.'

Book review pages soon sent me to T. James's bookshop, then in the dock area, and, with bicycle propped at the kerb, I gazed on the brightly-coloured dust jackets each concealing its individual harvest of aviation's riches. *Popular Flying* also featured ingeniously-designed rubber-powered flying models and advertised that ultimate joy, the crash-proof Frog Interceptor Fighter, for only five shillings; the fuselage was made of pressed aluminium with detachable, cellulose-protected special paper wings. The 11½ inch span model came in a compact travelling box with a compartment at one end in which engine and propeller fitted snugly, ready for winding from the adjacent gear via a small handle. Plastic kits were unknown but for two shillings a 1:72 scale wooden model of the beloved Hawker Fury could be obtained; being only rough formed it required finish-shaping, assembling and painting. Extending the range of types available the maker, A. J. Holladay, founded the Skybird League with a distinctive black flying bird motif on a yellow shield. Clubs formed across the country and I joined one run by Johnnie Rawlings, locally famed as a high speed skater at the ice-rink. He lived in a large house off The Avenue and here his parents allowed us the use of an empty attic where we set up our aerodrome. With cotton wool clouds suspended by threads from the ceiling and our favourite models poised between them and model hangars on the floor, we lived out our flying fantasies, only descending from the upper regions to consume sausage rolls for bodily nourishment; spiritual sustenance came, by way of a hand-cranked gramophone, from local trumpeter Nat Gonella who put 'Georgia on my mind' and inspired an early appreciation of the giants of traditional jazz.

The Air League of the British Empire, which aimed to foster airminded-ness, encouraged the formation of groups. Some of us banded together as Junior members to become No. 47 Flight , which helped when requesting visits to Service airstations at Gosport, Lee and Calshot. The League's official magazine, *Air Review*, sponsored drawing competitions, the prizes being free flights taken with the nearest local flying club; on one such early

DH60 Moth at Eastleigh, 1938.

introduction to the Hampshire Aeroplane Club, run by W. L. Gordon, the pilot of my Gipsy Moth chanced to be David Kay, designer of the Gyroplane which bore his name. A year or two later the Air League inaugurated the uniformed Air Training Corps cadet scheme.

Sometimes, in ambitious mood, I tried my hand at copying the superb cutaway drawings of aeroplanes being pioneered by *Flight* artist Max Millar. At school I had won no academic acclaim but was often awarded Hobbies prizes for drawings and paintings; I chose *Elementary Aeronautical Science* and the classics *Sagittarius Rising* (Cecil Lewis) and *Night Flight* (A. de St.-Exupery).

A benevolent destiny was directing me towards the aeroplane builders.

CHAPTER 2

SUPERMARINE (1937–1945)

A month after the untimely death of R. J. Mitchell, I left school. At my interview at the Woolston riverside factory of the Supermarine Aviation Works (Vickers) Ltd it was explained to my father that the company no longer took premium apprentices who paid for the privilege of being taught the trade: if they had done so I do not know whether he could have afforded the fees. Any optimistic pretension I may have had to become an instant draughtsman was quickly dashed. The short, plump apprentice supervisor, T. A. Locke, said, 'We like your drawings of aeroplanes but here it is necessary to show exactly where each rivet must go and to do that you will have to serve an apprenticeship in the works. You cannot become a good draughtsman without shop experience.' The fitting shop foreman arrived in clean, white dustcoat. Rather to my surprise he asked whether I had been taught Parisian French at school, then followed up by, 'If you come into my workshop I shall start by giving you all the tedious, dirty jobs we have in the factory. Do you still want to come?' 'Yes, sir!'

So in August 1937 I became, for a probationary period, a 'handy lad' and started work by punching a clock card at 7.30 each morning for an agreed sum of sixteen shillings (80p) per week. In truth it was a generous wage for the wondrous sight of the aeroplanes was immediate and the wealth of the experience was to last a lifetime. Like great galleons of old towered the last of the long line of Mitchell's flying-boats with their huge biplane superstructures. Spanning a full 85 feet from tip to tip and carrying her two big 900 hp Bristol Pegasus radial engines on the top plane, a Stranraer was a sight to stir the heart of any lad and, beyond the great hangar doors, the concrete launching slipway led down into the river.

The fitting shop (F shop) was on a balcony overlooking these monsters while they, in turn, overshadowed a handful of single-engined Walrus amphibious biplanes of a mere 45 foot span. Immediately below our balcony lay the machine shop, a dark labyrinth of mysterious and dangerous machinery to be hurried past with awe. It was succeeded by the sprawling main-plane assembly area known as 'P' shop. On its far side, overlooked by the elevated production offices, 'K' (Keel) shop disclosed among its unfinished Walrus hulls, strange steel structures called jigs and scattered around which lay diverse oval-shaped aluminium-alloy pressings. These were no flying boat frames but obviously destined for the magic fighter.

I knew that Supermarine had received an order for 310 Spitfires but I did not know of the subsequent request for 168 Walruses, two prototype Sea Otters, two new-design heavy bombers and yet more Spitfires. Until this time, the contract for the 17 Stranraers represented about the biggest order this small company had received and the magnitude of their unprecedented task must have seemed overwhelming; in the factory there was as yet little evidence of even a trickle of the flow of production that was to come.

From a 'glasshouse' office at one end of 'F' shop, the foremen, Harry Camm and George Figg, were able to survey their domain. It encompassed skilled fitters, drillers and toolmakers, a welder, girls operating engraving machines, inspectors and a fair number of 'handy lads', the whole sub-divided among a handful of supervisors. At the far end of the shop I was allocated a work bench with a sliding drawer and a vice. I came under the jurisdiction of Charlie Hemms, a short, dapper little chargehand with a moustache.

At first I found that, despite the undisputed merit of a good school education, it had prepared me for none of the immediate tasks I was now called upon to perform. I learnt to cut metal, file uniform surfaces, mark out and drill holes, sharpen drills, use a folding machine and a fly-press. I learnt to calculate bending allowances for developed shapes and, to avoid cracks, never to bend thin sheet metal over a block without a radius of, at least, the metal thickness. A steel wiring lug for Walrus wing-bracings may appear simple enough. In a folding machine the small flat strips of steel had to be bent up at each end to required angles which were checked by holding the lug up to the light and applying a pre-set angle gauge. Minor adjustment could be effected by a judicious tap with a hammer. Try as I might, my curved upturned lugs defied the tensile load straightness which was so essential.

Another machine employed a small vertical punch of about $3/16$ inch diameter which moved rapidly up and down while a hand-held steel template, with aluminium component attached, was moved round a guide in such a manner as to allow the punch to take bites out of the aluminium. The operator could then file smooth the spiky, gnawed edges until, flush with the hardened template, the component profile was complete. It may have been my youthful ignorance or an awed sense of the power of the machine which blinded me to the doubtless adequate though possibly misconceived directions of a harassed instructor and led me, in my panic, to operate this machine without fully understanding the necessary preliminaries of adjustment. The machine, technically and appropriately known as a 'nibbler', ran riot. When my hand reached the 'Off' switch it was obvious that a smallish but distinctly noticeable section had been nibbled from the master template. 'What the f . . . . . g hell are you doing?' said chargehand Charlie who suddenly reappeared at my elbow with another of his novitiates.

It was a time of change; whereas only a month before I had been a rather senior student at one of Southampton's better schools, now I was as the dust on the workshop floor.

Amidst the bustle of thriving 'F' shop an embryonic aircraft gun turret appeared. Almost daily a draughtsman came along and sat in it, deep in design thought; he was said to be a Mr Kimber, son of a man whose name was a byword in Southampton civic affairs. The turret was intended for the new four-engined bomber.

The coveted design office was hidden from shop-floor workers in the upper part of the recently-completed office block across the yard from the factory. The canteen lay in the same building and it could be reached from the 'F' shop gallery by way of a covered bridge over the main works entrance where uniformed gatekeepers actively investigated parcels anyone might bring in. Another bridge led over Hazel Road to the wood shop.

Aircraft people were jealously proud of their élite engineering skills. One afternoon each week, with three or four other 'handy lads', I would attend elementary classes, in a small office in the main block, taught by the apprentice supervisor who was nicknamed (Professor) 'Nimbus' after a cartoon character then appearing in a daily tabloid. Once, as we practised isometric drawing, the telephone rang. After a brief conversation our mentor replaced the receiver, turned to us and confided in shocked tones, 'A butcher! Wanted his son to come and work here!'

After a few probationary months, when I had been accepted for practical training as an aircraft engineer, my father received a satisfactory progress report which also stated, 'He is showing average ability in the shops'.

We apprentices were now accustomed to the early morning bicycle ride across the quiet town, skilled at avoiding the clanking trams, though sometimes taking a toss in their tracks. We relished the short river-crossings on the cable-guided floating bridge; from the port side we might see a flying-boat tugging at its moorings off the factory hard or to starboard a sleek grey destroyer at John I. Thornycroft's yard. Then, once past the uniformed guardians of the gates, slipping on our khaki dust coats, we became part of that colourful company of Supermarine: symbolic of authority, shop foremen wore white coats, inspectors green, women blue with hats to match, while maroon-coated progress-chasers scurried from shop to shop speeding the flow of urgently needed parts.

Discarded outdoor clothing was hung on hooked, rectangular-frame racks to be hoisted high in the roof, out of the way and inaccessible until lunchtime. There were no teabreaks; thermos flasks were smuggled in and it was possible to purchase, unofficially, twopenny bars of chocolate hidden deep in a certain fitter's bench drawer. Individual visits to toilet cubicles were entered in a book by an attendant and seven minutes was the allotted span for natural functions.

At the benches we acquired our first taste of freedom – schoolboys no longer yet learning to accept our own newfound discipline. Busily we filed our pieces of metal, hammered or folded them to shape, drilled them, submitted them to eagle-eyed inspectors and occasionally, to our chagrin, had them rejected and returned for correction.

On Saturday mornings the bustling activity stilled as the hour of noon approached. Benches were swept clean, vices and anvils generously oiled for the weekend until, as the hooter croaked its welcome message, we would join the hurrying throng pedalling or running to catch the earliest homeward ferry-boat. The two ferries which plied back and forth across the Itchen had a pivoted platform at each end for ease of entry and egress since the angular slope of the shelving, shingle beach would vary according to the state of the tide. Anxious to catch a departing ferry, many a rider would hurtle down the slope, dismount, and, bicycle in hand, take a flying leap across the widening gap. If he misjudged it he might burst a tyre on the platform's edge or, to our greater glee, drop into the water.

Away from the factory, weekly, the aeronautical press recorded the continuing demise of the biplane and the inexorable rise of the monoplane and how I cherished that beautiful Miles Kestrel wooden trainer. Technical controversy doubted the possibility of aeroplanes ever achieving the speed of sound. From the library, I borrowed an exciting book on rockets by Willey Ley. Captivated by the boldness of such endeavour and seduced by the colourfully imaginative artist's impressions of flight in outer space, I was saddened at the conclusions that, due to lack of suitable fuels to give a high enough escape velocity, there appeared to be no immediate prospect of progress in space. Oh, who dares predict?

Despite the ever greater emphasis on production as the rearmament programme accelerated the company was enlightened enough to allow its apprentices one day off each week to attend classes at the University College (now the University of Southampton) at a time when the practice was by no means universal among engineering firms. In addition, I attended two extra evening classes each week. At one, quiet-spoken, serious-minded Harry Tremelling ('Trem') from the firm's drawing office taught engineering drawing and aircraft construction; at first we copied blue-prints of parts of the old Southampton flying-boat, graduating to methods of finding its all-important centre of gravity. Then one evening the kindly Cornishman pulled up a chair and showed me how to calculate the capacity and thence centre of buoyancy of a seaplane float. At the other class, mould-loft foreman Don Snook instructed us in the theory and practice of full-scale lofting with its inter-relation of vertical and horizontal cutting planes to achieve faired shapes from which any desired intermediate or cant frame could be plotted. Both classes laid foundations of useful skills that were to last a lifetime.

In continuance of my training I was transferred to the wing shop. The excitement of the move was tempered with some misgivings due to the tough reputation of foreman Jim Weedy. Indeed the very day I started work in 'P' shop my immediate post-lunch task was to clear paint-clogged tapped holes in nut-rings secured to a completed Spitfire spar; the leading edge torsion box lay nose down in a wheeled trolley directly outside the foreman's office. 'Big Jim' had put on his white coat and stood, legs apart and shoulders hunched, glowering at me. He came over, took the tapwrench from my nervous grasp, carefully completed the hole I had been in danger of cross-threading and, with a kindly muttered 'Be careful son', moved on. I breathed again.

Experience bred confidence and I was soon happily engaged in assembling channel webs to the telescopic square-section tubular booms which made up the Spitfire's main spar. The ¼ inch fixing bolts on the early machines were aluminium alloy and would snap like carrots if overtightened. A painted label at the end of each assembly table gave the production identification; they were single figure numbers – numbers which ultimately would reach over 22,000. When the plain nuts had been tightened, protruding bolt ends had to be cut back almost flush with the nut to allow locking by three centre-punch indents equally spaced on the thread junction of bolt and nut. A tool was provided, rather like a box spanner, which guided an end-cutting drill in a hand-held drilling machine.

In contrast to the fitting shop, life in 'P' shop was more of a nomadic existence where one had to follow the job. I no longer had my own little territory of personal bench and vice. From now on thus it would always be. Beneath the balcony and behind the foreman's office a large drilling jig had been installed to accommodate spars during the operation of boring the critical seven large holes which would secure each wing to the fuselage. One morning two operators assigned to this important task apparently misapplied the handed drill guide plates, bored holes incorrectly and scrapped a spar; by lunchtime they had been dismissed and were gone.

As production was in the early stages, shortages sometimes occurred and an apprentice and his skilled fitter 'mate' might be temporarily without a job. It was a miserably uncomfortable experience, hovering amongst the leading edges trying to look busy while Big Jim roamed his empire.

For a time I helped a toolmaker building new spar assembly tables. He was boring holes in the heavy steel channel using a large two-handled electric drilling machine, known to us as a 'gut buster' because a bodily applied powerful push was needed to achieve penetration. The twist drill

broke and a fragment flew up nicking his face and narrowly missing an eye.

Less hazardous was assembly work where a hand reamer would suffice to merely clean out pre-drilled holes. Eagerly I would scuttle up the iron staircase to the balcony stores where many a gullible greenhorn had been sent for a long weight (wait). Returning with an armful of girder nose-ribs, I enjoyed the creative thrill of construction as we attached them to the newly-completed spars. Our task complete, the skeletal leading edge was ready for others to fit the thick 14G (.08″) alloy nose skins which came already press-formed to incorporate the tricky root end dihedral kink. Top and bottom panels, first prepared by the addition of spanwise 'Z' stiffeners, were clecoed in position and butted together on to an internal nosing strip. Then the deafening rattle of busy riveting teams reverberated round the factory as flush rivets were hammered home to complete the strong 'D' shaped leading edge torsion box.

This was then placed nose down in a vertical, wing assembly jig, its lone, tapered pintle pointing upwards ready to receive the oleo undercarriage leg, while the rest of the relatively light wing structure was built on. Inboard, on starboard planes, spindly fabrications made way for the radiator; beside them yawned the cavernous gap of the wheel well; next, incredibly in this slim framework, spaces were found for four .303 machine

The High Speed Spitfire N17 shows its modified outline (streamlined windscreen) and shorter rounded wing tips in the Supermarine hangar, 1939.

guns. The addition of detachable wing tips would perfect the flawless curves after the wing was removed from the jig.

The first solitary production Spitfire was delivered to No. 19 Squadron at Duxford by Jeffrey Quill in August, 1938. The following month saw the 'Munich Crisis'. My charge-hand in 'P' shop told us we would now 'have to work like hell' and, as the influx of new employees continued, this apprentice found himself teaching wing assembly operations to an untutored railway fitter. But for me it was soon time for another change.

Alongside the company's new office block, a stone jetty served as an employees' small car park where I often admired the sharp-edged racy lines of an Invicta. Across the road in a roofed shed we daily left our bicycles in racks. The cycle shed adjoined Don Snook's mould loft with its plywood scrieve boards and, suspended from the roof, a mock-up of an abandoned twin-engined fighter. Turning inland from the shoreline route, past the corner sweet shop, Sea Road led under the railway bridge, steeply uphill to Peartree Green from whence a four mile journey brought one to the pleasant municipal grass aerodrome past the perimeter of which the upper reaches of the Itchen meandered.

To enter the spacious interior of those 1918 wooden-framed hangars was akin to stepping into a cathedral for here was the ultimate glory. A row of half a dozen or more trestled fuselages, with wings and tails attached, were tidily aligned in echelon along one whitewashed wall. Their brown and green camouflage paint was emblazoned with yellow-ringed red, white and blue roundels; light-green access doors hung below the cockpit on each port flank while radio doors were propped open behind. Small formers joined fuselage to wing, promise of fillets yet to come. Neither tanks nor cowlings were in place but gleaming black Rolls Royce Merlins nestled in the green engine bearers, the silvery splines of their propeller shafts thrust forward; more engines lay on stands grouped on the hangar floor. Between the aeroplanes were stepladders, small benches with vices attached and scattered tool-boxes: among all this paraphernalia overalled workers went about their tasks. Framed in the huge doorway which opened on to the airfield, brightly glistening, smelling of fresh paint, oil and glycol, was the most beautiful thing I had ever seen in my life – a newly-completed Spitfire.

Wearing a white boiler suit in place of khaki dust coat, I was privileged to assist in joining the graceful wings, which I had helped build, to the sleek fuselages. The wings, port and starboard separately, were supported on trestles. In response to a hail from the wing-fitter, half a dozen nearby hands would leave their immediate task to bend beneath a wing, bearing its weight on their shoulders. By shuffling along, heads down, the group would contrive, at shouted commands, to guide the protruding spar ends into a gap in the fuselage stub booms. Temporary undersize drift bolts would be hammered into some of the seven large attachment holes, three in the top boom four in the lower, allowing the final closely fitting bolts to be carefully installed, one by one, later. One young man on this work did not return after a weekend; he was reputed to have been killed training with the RAF volunteer reserve: a grim reminder that the pilot build-up was accelerating too.

I was teamed as 'mate' to a skilled fitter named Jim, a tall gangling young man who told me he had been maintenance engineer with the Spartan biplane, *Island Queen*, at Shanklin. My mind shot back to my first flight and my world began to shrink.

On the early Spitfires, the engine coolant radiator was fitted beneath only the starboard wing and the innovative arrangement passed air from the inlet into a divergent duct, it was slowed through the honeycomb matrix and accelerated out by convergent ducting at the rear, a hinged exit flap controlling the rate of cooling. To secure the radiator fairing, fixing screws had to be inserted 'blind' into anchor nuts in the curved duct. This entailed thrusting an arm through the narrow intake from an awkward squatting position underneath the wing and groping for the holes and sometimes invoking the aid of a small mirror; it proved an onerous task.

While I struggled with recalcitrant screws, work was proceeding nearby on a specially-modified, blue-painted, high-speed Spitfire being prepared for an attempt on the World Speed Record. Once, a pilot landed a Spitfire with the wheels up and in an adjoining hangar, less routinely, we each did our usual job in reverse. By observing daily flight tests I learnt how 'one wing low' flying characteristics could be trimmed out by the rigger attaching, with dope and fabric, a short length of cable to the top surface of the low aileron at the trailing edge.

One lunchtime we strolled along to the Hampshire Aeroplane Club to inspect a neat little light aeroplane parked outside. It was the diminutive Chilton monoplane, designed and built by Dalrymple and Ward at Hungerford. A spring day at the end of March 1939 brought a visitor from further afield when Major Alexander de Seversky arrived from the USA, with his stubby, barrel-shaped elliptical-winged fighter, the Sev 2PA. We stayed on after work to see him fly a Spitfire while our Jeffrey Quill tried out the American aeroplane. Whilst exciting, it seemed to lack the dainty grace of the Spitfire although later it was to achieve lasting fame when developed by designer Alexander Kartvelli into the P47 Thunderbolt. The Major was full of praise for the Spitfire and as, we heard, he next visited Germany where he flew the Messerschmitt 109, he became the first pilot to fly the rival types in peacetime.

When the large Spitfire contract had been secured, Vickers dynamic General Manager at Woolston, Trevor Westbrook, had set up a production office to design jigs and tools, expanded the labour force, and organised an extensive system of sub-contracting before he transferred to Weybridge shortly before I joined. Indeed, when I started work, tales of his forceful presence were still reverberating throughout the factory. It was to fill a vacancy in the recently-formed jig and tool design office, and thanks to recommendation from 'Trem', that I was sent back to the main Woolston works to join the small team of draughtsmen comprising 'Mac' Macdonald, Harry Richardson, Stafford Coates, Eric Warren, Paul Sear, Don Bruce, Ewart John, George Bond, 'Serge' Newton and Ranchford Evans. In overall charge was the Chief Planning Engineer, John Bull. The works-staff offices embraced planning, rate-fixing, purchasing, sub-contracting and works engineers, all situated in glass-fronted offices on the balcony. Our office overlooked, on one side 'P' shop and on the other 'K' shop.

At last I was a trainee draughtsman and was given command of a 54 inch vertical draughting machine complete with built-in sliding Tee-square and angular-adjustable graduated rulers. At first I had to draw, for the record, simple drill jigs, usually from freehand sketches 'Mac' had done to expedite their manufacture. Many were of the 'nutcracker' type where the work was clamped by a hinged lid only as long as the operator gripped together two short handles. Graduating to more complex work, it became common practice to initially draw to scale the aircraft part and build up the drawing of a jig around it. When jigs were required to facilitate manufacture of larger, contoured components a draughtsman would have to plot curves using the co-ordinates of the aircraft's basic lines: the value of Don Snook's lofting training became apparent. Curiously, shipbuilding practice carried over into the Spitfire fuselage geometry where horizontal cutting planes were annotated as WL (Water Lines).

My initial regrets at not being in the main aircraft drawing office had been countered by assurance that in the TDO (Tool Drawing Office) I would be able to see all their mistakes; so it proved but, of course, we made our mistakes too. Due to aircraft drawing ambiguities, an error was built into the fuselage assembly jigs for the two four-engined bomber prototypes; as it was too late to change things both fuselages were constructed and accepted six inches too short in length.

Meanwhile, out in the factory all was not well. Wings were not pouring in from the sub-contractors and the company had been forced to build their own additional wing jigs to meet the demand. A large, new factory, known as the Itchen Works, was built a third of a mile upstream from the main complex and Spitfire fuselages were packed into it for Stage II operations while awaiting wings.

This then was the situation when the long-expected conflict began. I went to war armed with a Tee-square and a book of Chambers seven figure log tables because slide rules lacked the accuracy necessary for our trigonometric calculations and the TDO could muster but one crude, hand-cranked mechanical calculator used to check our dimensioned drawings for errors. It was a different war from the last: two Territorial Army contemporaries who promptly disappeared at the outbreak were back at the factory within a week: aircraft production skills took precedence over all else.

One day Harry gave me another job. He brought with him an experimental short length of curved plate which had been formed to fit round a wing leading edge. A hole had been cut in it and a few inches of large diameter tube welded in. I was asked to design a turning fixture to hold the component while the tube was bored and screw-threaded and so realised that the Spitfire was becoming cannon conscious.

From my modest niche in the TDO I was less aware of the extraordinary dramatic events which took place in early 1940 when, following the Nuffield motor car organisation's inability to master the intricacies of aircraft con-struction, Vickers formally took over management of the huge new Castle Bromwich Spitfire 'shadow' factory and placed young S. P. Woodley from Supermarine in charge.

After the long 'phoney war', our work began to be interrupted by sporadic air raids. Once, following a raid warning signal, we unhurriedly left the office to join the chattering throng strolling towards the shelters beside the Itchen Works. Two aeroplanes were flying down the river at only a few thousand feet when, to our utter disbelief, a stick of bombs splashed into the water. From that moment on, at the siren song we always broke into a run.

But when the great trumpets sounded there was no St. Crispin's day for us. From our worm's eye view of the thin white contrails criss-crossing in the bright-blue summer sky where the immortal élite lived their fleeting finest hour, it was difficult to see much or to know what was happening even when momentous events were quite close. On 16 August Flt Lt James Nicolson, after persistently attacking Bf 109s and severely burnt on face and hands, abandoned his blazing Hurricane and took to his parachute to descend at Millbrook, a mere four miles from Supermarine; for his action he received Fighter Command's only Victoria Cross.

The proximity of such battles, the nagging awareness that we were sitting on an obvious and vulnerable waterfront target, destroyed any faith we might have had in the air raid shelters sited close to the works. So, urged by the siren's chilling wail, in the late afternoon of Tuesday, 24 September, my friend and I hurried from the factory deciding to avoid the shelters and run up the steep hill, under the railway bridge, towards open-common land. As we panted upwards, hearts pounding, local Bofors guns opened fire;

skywards I had a brief glimpse of shell bursts around diving aircraft; trouble was very imminent. At the road fork I had decided to take the left path when, glancing up again, I saw a bomb immediately overhead glinting in the sunlight. A split-second change of mind caused me to dive ahead and crouch outside a small brick-built first-aid post in the road Y junction just as big 'Serge' Newton appeared from the other side: at that instant fate granted me a full life span. As if in slow motion, I watched the roof of a house lifting into the air, then we were showered with dust and peppered with débris amidst the all-engulfing sound and stupefying terror of explosions. When the air had cleared we saw the houses on either side of us flattened; the bombs had straddled us. Astounded to be still alive, we entered the first-aid post and when we had calmed down a little we helped rescue workers on the demolished houses for a time before returning home.

Years after, I learned that the diving aircraft had been Messerschmitt Bf 110s of Erprobungsgruppe 210 which had flown straight in from the Cherbourg peninsula and for which daring attack Martin Lutz was posthumously awarded a Knights Cross since he was killed three days later leading a raid on Parnall Aircraft at Yate. The factory was not seriously damaged but a shelter had been hit which accounted for many of the 90 deaths in the area.

Two days later, 59 He 111s of KG 55, escorted by 70 Bf 110s, flew straight up the Solent and dropped 70 tons of bombs during a precision 'carpet attack' in a single run across the factory. This time there had been a little longer warning and we lay in a prickly holly-leaf-lined ditch on Freemantle Common, well away from the works, listening to the crack of the Bofors and sensing the sickening earth tremors of exploding bombs. The blonde from the corner sweet shop outside the factory gates took refuge near us, flat on her face in her smart white coat underneath a lorry. Next day, wearing borrowed tin hats, we were allowed into the ruins of that ill-fated factory for the last time to pick our way over the rubble into the drawing office to collect our belongings. Bomb blast had dispersed most things but from among the broken glass I salvaged a setsquare, now with a bomb-splinter hole in it; I still use it.

Three completed Spitfires were destroyed, more than twenty damaged. The two bomber fuselages were badly damaged and the project abandoned. Lord Beaverbrook arrived and ordered immediate dispersal of all production facilities. The fourth floor of Southampton's swish Polygon Hotel was requisitioned next day for Supermarine staff, led by Works Engineer, L. G. Gooch, to start planning the dispersal. The nation was fighting for survival and Spitfires were desperately needed. The planners were told to use the tradesmen's entrance but, seeking enlightenment as to the whereabouts of the jig and tool office, I left my bicycle in the forecourt and was making my way up the main staircase when accosted by a neatly-dressed stranger. He asked if I was one of the 'Spitfire boys' and offered his professional help, should we need it. 'I run a glove cleaning service here in the hotel', he said.

After a brief sojourn in huts in the University College grounds we were

"I bought a 500 cc Norton CS1."

moved about seven miles north of Southampton to the large country house at Hursley Park which was requisitioned from Sir George Cooper of Strongs' Breweries as the company's executive offices. It sheltered the Supermarine team throughout the war and for a dozen years after. Daily, a fleet of green Hants and Dorset buses shuttled employees between the Park and their homes; they brought them to a peaceful world removed from factory noise and the terror of bombs.

In the great house the oak-panelled walls and staircases were boarded over for protection. Temporarily, Lady Cooper continued to live in a restricted area while office staff spread into the other huge rooms. We tool designers were located in a top-storey room at the eastern end, overlooking the high-walled vegetable garden; it was possible to climb out through the windows and sit in the sun, precariously perched on flat areas of roof. Beneath our eyrie, the glass-domed roof of the ballroom covered the aircraft drawing office. The spacious basement kitchens were taken over by canteen staff and we ate in small rooms on the opposite side of the long stone-paved corridor. While wartime rationing limited variety, I revelled in supplemented cheese fritters since these were not popular with all. The corridor led into the stable yard, the buildings of which became head-quarters for the increasingly important transport department as dispersed production spun its web across Southern England. Wild deer roamed the Park and, hearing shooting one day, from a limited window view, it distressed me to see one of these lovely creatures fall, although it meant off-ration venison would soon be on sale in the village butcher's shop.

Two or three fighter pilots were sent to the Park on a production and morale-boosting visit. As all the Supermarine staff gathered round to listen to them I stood partway up the staircase, deeply moved. They stood near the doorway between the ballroom and the great hall, very young, be-medalled, immaculate in best uniform; they were superb.

Sometimes our work took us on visits to outlying manufacturing units by train or car. At Chattis Hill, where the racing gallops had been taken-over as a Spitfire test airfield, I found myself stranded for an hour or two waiting for routine transport home. Somehow I managed to cadge a lift back to Eastleigh in the company's hack, a Miles Falcon with forward sloping windscreen, flown by an RAF uniformed pilot carrying 'Norway' on his shoulder flash; we slipped down through a barrage-balloon-spattered sky for a landing, after which I made my way home full of excitement.

I bought a 350 cc Panther 'sloper' motorcycle, taught myself to ride and then bought a 500 cc Norton CSI with overhead camshaft for £60; it was often ridden straddled askew as I turned my head to sniff in the aromatic odours of burnt racing Castrol R.

In January 1941 I had written a letter of enquiry concerning the Royal Observer Corps. It got lost for only at the end of May came a reply signed by Peter Masefield of *The Aeroplane*. Summoned to the Common at Copythorne village, I was interviewed by the splendidly-bearded, elderly Chief Observer, Major D. H. B. Harfield, who was a solicitor and Southampton coroner. Given a striped armlet and a black beret as badges of office, I became a part-time Observer at Post Fox 1 a few miles west of Southampton, taking my turn at 4 or 8 hour duty shifts because, throughout the war the posts were manned for 24 hours every day. Our task was to notify the passage of all aircraft. We always worked in pairs, one to manoeuvre a rather primitive but effective sighting instrument which gave a geographical grid plot, the other to keep a listening watch and report plots to Winchester HQ by breast-mounted telephone. In the course of the war 32 men served with Fox 1. We were a mixed crew from all walks of life so contrasting conversations helped pass the long reaches of many a quiet but sleepless night.

Experience had shown authority the increasing importance of instant recognition of different types of aeroplane and here, although wearing glasses, I came into my own because of my intense interest. Nevertheless I was sometimes amazed at the sharp eyesight of the countrymen who would point out distant aircraft which I could barely discern with binoculars. Each post ran regular training meetings using epidiascopes to flash aircraft silhouettes on to a screen for the tiniest fraction of a second, yet this proved ample time for identification. Because so many younger men were in the armed forces, observers tended to be of more mature years and, of course, in general they lacked specialised aircraft technical knowledge. In these circumstances I began to acquire a reasonable reputation at aircraft recognition and when national proficiency tests were introduced I became entitled to wear a woven Spitfire arm badge on the RAF blue uniform I now wore.

At Hursley Park, in the grounds near the house, a large temporary building had been erected beneath the trees and draped with camouflage

ROC Post 3/F1 at Stagbury Mount. Chief Observer Major D. H. B. Harfield, Observer R. Rainsley, Leading Observer J. O. Isaacs.

netting; it housed about 150 people of the design drawing office. Between it and the house a smaller wooden hut was built close alongside the vegetable garden wall to accommodate the TDO whose numbers peaked at about 20; down we had come from our lofty perch. At one entrance to the Park, near the village school, a newly-erected large hangar now served for the construction of prototype aeroplanes.

At one stage, about the middle of the war, a friendly new tool draughtsman joined our ranks. Much to my surprise, Harry told us he was an RAF pilot with Coastal Command; presumably there was a surplus of pilots then and he reverted to his earlier trade. He stayed for some months before mysteriously disappearing again. A few weeks later, alerted by the sound of aero-engines, I rushed to my window where, by leaning out and looking up, I could see a small patch of sky between our hut and the brick wall. I was just in time to glimpse an all-white Vickers Warwick flash overhead at 100 feet: Harry was back with the RAF we decided. Another day, on the lawn behind the house, I watched in wonder as an American Sikorsky hovered vertically down to settle; it was the first helicopter I ever saw.

In 1942 my observer post moved a few miles to a new site on top of Stagbury Mount at Furzely on the edge of the New Forest. That same year a new airfield was completed under cover of the Forest at Stoney Cross, a few miles south. The following summer its RAF Albemarles often passed overhead but in March 1944 when the USAAF took over, large spectactular formations of Lightning twin-boom fighters began orbiting the area.

Now, I had become Leading Observer instructor to our little band. We had always been honoured to wear Royal Air Force blue and, in our small way, support the flying men. Consequently at training meetings we occasionally welcomed talks by operational pilots. One such chat came from a USAAF officer who promised we should visit his unit at Stoney Cross a few weeks hence. We duly arrived at the airfield, on a wet and windy Sunday, to find our host seemed a little pre-occupied. Nevertheless we were ferried about the station in Jeeps to examine the Lightnings. Some had the inboard-side engine cowlings polished to a mirror finish so that the pilot could visually check by reflection that the nose-wheel was down for landing. We were told that a mysterious spate of broken wing tip lights had puzzled the engineer officer before it was discovered that the boys had been playing at nudging wing tips in flight! One Lightning bore a great jagged rent in a wing leading edge from which trailed yards of thin cable inadvertently snatched out of France the previous day while low-level train busting: I broke off a piece as a souvenir. It was curious to note that all the aeroplanes were having black and white vertical stripes painted on the fuselages. Two days later on Tuesday, 6 June, 'D' Day, I understood the officer's reticence and have ever admired him for keeping his promise in such secret circumstances.

On 26 July an Aircraft Recognition Instructors Course assembled at Southport and for a week or two I lived and worked with the Royal Air Force. We lived in a requisitioned hotel in that holiday town, the ROC element receiving sergeant status. Daily we marched to other impressed hotels to attend lectures and give lectures; I enjoyed every moment. Given a choice of compulsory sports one afternoon, it amused me to play bowls (my father's game in maturity) with young fighter pilots who were evidently following in Drake's footsteps. On returning home, having been informed that I was the first observer from my Group to be classified A.1, I was further amused to learn on the grapevine that bets had been placed at local HQ as to whether I would achieve that grading.

As the war's end approached other visits became possible to Service airfields. At one, the observers of F.1 chanced upon an isolated Flying Fortress and were not discouraged by their airfield guide from climbing in, with difficulty. We drank in the scene, exactly as portrayed in pictures – two big waist gun apertures, tiny ball turret suspended beneath the fuselage, maps of England lying up front. As we clambered about this great chariot of war, the American crew suddenly appeared, swung themselves aboard with casual disregard of our crowding presence and we had barely time to scramble out before the four Wright engines were fired-up and it

41

trundled off we knew not where. Another time we did fly, squatting on the empty floor of a boxy-fuselaged Avro York during brief excursion over the Forest.

Luck granted me an interesting experience for which some people pay a lot of money. I was always excited by art and its techniques so was intrigued when my Chief Observer, a fine figure of a man, was chosen to represent the ROC for an oil painting by an Official War Artist. The artist, William Dring, chose not to paint a formal portrait but opted instead for an action picture on our post site. From the peripheral well of the sunken observation post, his viewpoint looked upwards at the Major and me as we stood on the raised platform in operational pose: for an hour he quickly sketched in crayons. Next day, with a simulated skyward gaze, I sat on a chair placed on a table in the Major's house while further facial detail was deftly depicted by the artist seated at floor level. Some weeks later it was fascinating to enter his garden studio near Winchester and view the large oil painting: after the war I saw it hanging in the Imperial War Museum.

When, thankfully, the conflict was all over, with hundreds more, in uniform, I went to London, slept in an underground bunk, received half an hour's march training from a Guardsman and marched past the King himself in the great Victory Parade.

In the autumn of 1945 The Royal Aircraft Establishment staged a remarkable Exhibition of German Aircraft and Equipment at Farnborough. Here on the runways, the black silhouettes and grainy photographs of the long war years came astoundingly to life. Laid out before us were real aeroplanes representing all the famous marques – Arado, Blohm and Voss, Dornier, Focke-Wulf, Heinkel, Junkers, Messerschmitt, Siebel, Fieseler, Horten and Flying Bombs and A4 rockets. In the hangars magnificent coloured drawings laid bare their innermost secrets. Static displays explained German constructional methods, materials and novel design features. Space was devoted to engines and rocket motors, radio and electrical devices, test instruments, navigation and auto controls, photographic equipment, gunsights, bombs, ammunition, turrets – all testimony to Teutonic technical competence.

On the airfield, of the many aeroplanes which were demonstrated in the air, none generated more interest than the legendary jets like the twin-engined Me 262 and the He 162 carrying its single BMW turbine mounted atop the fuselage. Sadly, it was the latter which marred the day with tragedy. As it cavorted over the field it seemed suddenly to go out of control, tumbling helplessly end over end. Agonized, we watched the chilling sight, all silently willing the pilot to eject, but the Volksjaeger had turned into a projectile as it plummeted vertically downwards towards an army barracks at nearby Aldershot. Momentarily a huge mushroom of flame and smoke erupted from behind the trees like a volcano; the watching crowds seemed to disperse and a hush fell over the airfield.

CHAPTER 3

YOUNG MAN'S FANCY (1945–1950)

In peacetime a young man's fancy turned to thoughts of flying and so began a brief flirtation with gliding when I attached myself to Airspeed test pilot Ron Clear's group at Portsmouth Airport. He owned the Abbott-Baynes Scud III which, in 1935, was considered a novel attempt to overcome the eternal problem of how best to launch a glider. Sir John Carden had designed an ingenious system employing a Villiers two-stroke engine; it reputedly gave 9 hp at 3,500 rpm for the short take-off run on the Scud's single recessed wheel. About ten minutes later, at 2,000 feet, the pilot could operate a crank in the cockpit to retract the engine and propeller cleanly into the fuselage thus converting the aircraft into a sailplane. If glider purists of the day were offended no heresy charge could be levelled against Ron as the engine had been removed and he used the 45½ foot span monoplane purely for soaring.

Bert Parslow owned its forerunner, the tiny unstable Scud II, which he once flew from Portsmouth to Hindhead. Its square-section fuselage was cunningly canted over at 45 degrees making it appear more streamlined as it presented a head-on diamond shape, the lowest longeron acting as landing keel. Ken Fripp owned a Kirby Kite and elderly Bert Dunning built his original 'Lancia', an interesting development of the Grunau Baby with flaps and enclosed cockpit.

A ground crew of would-be pilots supported this élite nucleus of aircraft owners with hopeful eye on the club assets comprising an aged German Kassel 20 single-seat trainer of uncertain origin and basic parts of a Dagling primary trainer.

The aircraft were kept in cave-like shelters secreted amongst the maze of ancient fortifications in a corner of the municipal airport; there was also a small workshop at Purbrook village a few miles distant.

Bert Parslow's Scud II.

Our launching problem was solved by the investment of £2 in an ancient but powerful open-chassis Buick obtained from a council employee who had been instructed to dump it in a scrapyard. It could be driven across the aerodrome towing a glider on the end of a few hundred feet of steel wire until, if the tow was fast enough, it soared aloft to be freed by the pilot pulling the release knob; greater launch heights became possible using an alternative winch system. A flanged steel drum was fabricated, to be bolted to one of the rear wheels of the Buick. With the motor-car stationary, its rear driving wheels were jacked clear of the ground and the differential locked. A suitable gear was engaged, the clutch let in, and on being pulled forward the glider rose as the cable was wound on to the drum. Success depended largely on the skill of the winch driver but as a safeguard against pilot failure to release the cable, a large axe was always on hand. In dire emergency it was the job of the winchman's assistant to sever the wire as it passed over a steel anvil while winding on to the drum.

On a long bank holiday weekend the untaxed Buick furtively left the airport precincts and was driven stealthily to 650 foot high Old Winchester Hill accompanied by the two Scuds in glider trailers. Here they were assembled and launched. At the end of a day's play the pilots called at a neighbouring farmhouse seeking permission to leave the gliders there overnight; they explained to the housewife that there had been no lift that day and the gliders had descended straightaway to the bottom of the hill.

The launching Buick on Old Winchester Hill, 5 August 1946.

'Oh my word, and did you escape?' said the good lady.

Then we could follow the ridge of the South Downs along the Brighton road, diverting to 700 foot Kithurst Hill, overlooking Storrington village, to apply the bunjee launch. The principle is to lay out on the ground a length of cotton-sheathed rubber shock cord, known as bunjee, in the form of the letter V, a steel ring being attached to its apex. The ring is slipped over a hook under the nose of the glider. The heaviest member of the group now lies on his stomach at the tail, firmly gripping the skid with leather-gloved hands. The free ends of the elastic rope are picked up by two four-man teams who walk away on diverging paths under the pilot's command. When he shouts 'Run' they accelerate their pace down the slope, stretching the bunjee until the anchor man can no longer resist the pull of the skid. The glider is snatched from his hands and catapulted off the edge of the hill like an arrow, free to soar for as long as the skill of the pilot and the whim of the winds allow.

Of necessity the most suitable soaring ridges slope away ever more sharply from the crest. I never enjoyed that dangerous headlong charge down an increasingly steep hill; it was suggestive of that little ball, balanced precariously on top of a hemisphere, which is sometimes drawn to illustrate the meaning of the term 'unstable' as applied to an aeroplane which, when disturbed from a particular condition of flight, tends to move ever further away from its original position.

Back on the flat, 'neutrally stable', aerodrome my turn came for what was euphemistically termed a 'ground slide' when I was towed behind the moving Buick on a short length of cable. Seated in the old Kassel 20 and feeling very much alone, I gazed ahead striving to keep the wings level and the craft straight. Pulling gently back on the stick, I was horrified to find the

Bert Dunning built his original Lancia.

ground rapidly falling away; I appeared to be at an enormous height, the edge of the airfield fast approaching with the uninviting waters of Langstone Harbour beyond. Hastily I pulled the release knob − I must have been at least ten feet high, perhaps 15, or even 20! My abrupt arrival back on the airfield was heralded by the sound of splintering plywood as my feet went through the bottom of the fuselage.

I booked a gliding holiday at Treforest in Wales but this was cancelled; private flying seemed to take some time to revive in the aftermath of war.

Meanwhile, despite its happy spirit, it became obvious that the group was not geared for serious training so frustration caused me to invest £80 of savings and a two week holiday in an attempt to obtain a power pilot's 'A' licence.

Late in 1938, a British company was formed to build under licence a trim little 55 hp high wing cabin monoplane with side-by-side seating for two. Known as the Taylorcraft, it had been designed by American engineer C. G. Taylor (also designer of the tandem seat Cub). Fitted with a 90 hp Cirrus Minor I for RAF use, the type was designated Auster I: civil versions were produced as the 'Plus D'. The prototype Auster I, now in the civil guise of G-AHAF, was one of several of the type operating in the metallic silver-blue with red nose colours of the Wiltshire School of Flying at High Post Aerodrome when I presented myself for flying tuition on 2 September, 1946.

High Post was a grass field north of Salisbury and it was here that Squadron Leader J. E. Doran-Webb was attempting to re-establish the flying school he had inaugurated in 1931 and run successfully using, inter alia, Redwing biplanes and Taylorcraft Plus Cs. Although post-war flying had only started in April 1946 a total of 42 'A' licences had been obtained while

Daily Inspection on Scud II at Portsmouth, with the Kassel 20 behind.

the flying time amounted to 1,267 hours. The equipment consisted of six ex-RAF Austers, G-AHAE, -AF, -KN, -KO, -UG and -UH, an Auster V.J-I G-AGVP and a Miles Magister G-AHKP, all of which obtained Certificates of Airworthiness in the club's workshops. The three instructors were Flt Lt K. W. Birt, DFC, B. E. J. Hawkins and G. A. Lovell; all were Civil Air Guard trained by the club before the war and all served as instructors in the RAF during the war. At first I was mainly assigned to the down-to-earth kindly Bert Hawkins. To him I brought my academic flying knowledge, largely gleaned from Lt Col G. L. P. Henderson's *A Complete Course of Practical Flying*, written in 1930.

Little had changed and the flying techniques for the Moth biplanes, which I had studied so assiduously, applied equally well to the simple Auster Is which were devoid of flaps or radio, as hardly any airfields had Air Traffic Control, airways were non-existent and there were practically no control zone or danger areas. Even Heathrow was then operating from a temporary red-brick control tower, the administrative and operational staff worked from pre-fabs and passengers were accommodated in a series of large tents.

The Auster's wooden propeller had to be hand swung to start the Cirrus Minor I after priming from the substantial brass Ki-gas pump in the cockpit. The level of the ten imperial gallon fuel tank ahead of the instrument panel was indicated by a wire in a tube sticking up from the top of the tank immediately in front of the windscreen. With a fuel consumption of five gallons an hour, 90 minutes was considered a safe endurance. The tail trim control consisted of a short lever between the two rather cramped seats; at the tail it was connected by cables to small separate trimming surfaces canti-levered from the fuselage beneath the tailplane – a somewhat unorthodox arrangement.

Ron Clear's Scud III at Old Winchester Hill.

Being fairly tall, I quickly found that I was destined to suffer from 'Auster-shin', brought about by the low set control column yoke tube running across the cockpit to which both sticks were attached and which moved aft and downwards when you pulled the stick back. Thus, when holding the stick back to taxi, or to keep the tail on the ground after landing, bumpy surface oscillations caused a series of sharp painful blows on the shins.

With fuel on, both magneto switches on contact, trimmer neutral, mixture rich, the centrally-mounted American-style push-pull throttle had only to be pushed firmly forward and the miracle of flight would commence. Climbing speed was 65 mph at full throttle and, at 2,100 rpm, the cruise was 90 mph. The approach was made at 60–65 mph, excessive height being side-slipped off if necessary before the final flare and hold-off for a three-point landing. All in all it was a delightful little aeroplane and, I felt, much more fun than the later, heavier, flapped Austers; I was to retain its essential philosophy of simplicity years later in my own aeroplanes.

Steeped in aeronautical history, the sparsely-populated area of Salisbury Plain has been described as 'perhaps the best stretch of country in England for the training of aviators'. Larkhill was the earliest centre of military flying and, following the constitution of the Royal Flying Corps in April 1912, the Central Flying School was started a few miles away at Upavon while a new aerodrome was built at Netheravon. The earliest casualties of the new Service, Captain Eustace Lorraine and Staff Sergeant R. H. V. Wilson, died on the Plain when their fast two-seater Nieuport

Magister G-AHKP of the Wiltshire School of Flying, High Post, 1946.

Auster I of the Wiltshire School of Flying at Thruxton.

monoplane dived off a turn into the ground near Stonehenge, the first of several accidents which caused the War Office to ban the use of monoplanes by the RFC.

My September holiday over that favoured training ground was sometimes beset with wind and rain but such elemental handicaps ensured early familiarity with buffeting by rough weather. High Post lay close in line with Boscombe Down's main long runway from which an occasional enormously-powerful, fearsome beast would streak over the little grass airfield which we shared with the Supermarine Experimental Flight Test Department where the company's first jet, the prototype Attacker, was being tested. To reduce the circuit hazards arising from the proximity of the Aeroplane and Armament Experimental Establishment, on weekdays we left our home field to detour round Boscombe Down and practise landings on the disued wartime airfield at Thruxton.

Identified by an untidy perimeter collection of wrecked abandoned Horsa gliders, Thruxton had three runways of standard pattern, a single black T2 hangar and a derelict air-traffic control tower as mute reminder of its former days of Service glory. I used to wonder how many uniformed, brave men, gripped by an amalgam of excitement and fear, had trod that ground which I grew to love so well; for, apart from its use by ground attack

B. E. J. Hawkins, flying instructor.

fighters, the proud paratroops of the Bruneval raid had emplaned from there in No. 51 Squadron's Whitleys.

Much has been written on the psychology of flying training and many reach a depth of despair at some stage in the learning process. An aeroplane is in a state of delicate balance at all times, poised in three dimensional space by those four variable opposing forces, lift and weight, thrust and drag, and it can only be kept so by skilful co-ordination of stick, rudder and throttle. The situation is further influenced by uncontrollable natural forces such as winds and rising or descending air masses. Also, subconscious awareness that the aeroplane must be kept going, controlled that is, until the flight has reached a successful conclusion introduces additional mental pressures.

It is not too difficult for a beginner to master straight and level flight once its secret is understood; Lt Col Henderson summed it up as 'sit still and hold still'. Given the philosophy of allowing the pupil to learn by his mistakes, the instructor's problem is knowing how late he dare leave corrective action to prevent catastrophe.

I was having difficulty with landings. We had flown over to deserted Thruxton, Flt Lt Birt and I, and to begin with I was not keeping the little aeroplane straight on take-off. Suddenly he took control once we left the ground and deliberately held the nose down so that we rushed at nearby woods in a manner which had me flinching from the upward groping branches so close below the flimsy fabric of the fuselage. 'You must keep it straight with the rudder, like this', he snapped, savagely kicking on first left and then right rudder while the nose yawed from side to side across the trees. Rather shocked at such apparent display of irresponsibility and being unaccustomed to other than a normal take-off and climb-out, I had to admit to myself that he had forcibly made the point.

On the next circuit, again I left the landing flare too late so that we flew into the ground and were tossed back a dozen feet into the air by the tyres' resilience, the airspeed rapidly decayed towards a full stall. Feeling thoroughly ashamed of myself, I sank into my seat, miserably wondering how I could ever get it right and, mentally giving up the unequal struggle, waited to see what my instructor would do. The poor little Auster hung poised ready to drop heavily back to earth which, I mused, would surely break the undercarriage at the very least even if we escaped physical injury.

My reverie was rudely interrupted as I became aware of an urgently insistent voice hissing in my ear, 'Throttle, throttle, throttle.' Belatedly realising with instant alarm that my instructor was not going to do anything about it, I rammed forward the little disc-handled rod between us and, as we staggered to safety, away from the ground, noted with amazement that he had not even moved his hands near the controls: he had gambled on my obeying his voiced command. I was then told in no uncertain terms that I had control of the aircraft and I had to sort it out fast for, when alone, no-one else could do so. It was a chastening experience but I never forgot that lesson. Every instructor has to satisfy himself that if any landing is at all in doubt the pupil will always respond instantly, like Pavlov's dogs, and push the throttle open to go round again; if he is not certain on that point he dare not send him solo.

I did a lot more practice landings. 'Pull back on the stick just a little and make that first check (of the descent) when the ground is as far below you as if you were on top of a double-decker bus,' said Bert Hawkins. As the descent slowed and we sank lower the stick was eased very gently further back. Finally, 'Stick back, back – don't let the wheels touch,' said the voice beside me. 'Right, now keep the stick hard back in your balls.'

It was difficult to get it just right for it required a sympathetic feel for the aeroplane's situation. I developed the habit of sitting on the top deck of local buses, imagining I was in the Auster starting the landing check or I would pace the streets thinking it out, tortured with impatience at myself until the next lesson. But when the hard-sought skill suddenly came, the sense of satisfaction was beyond belief, and, oh the rare joy of pulling off an occasional 'daisy cutter' when the transition from air to earth was so perfectly right that one was uncertain as to the exact moment the wheels touched until there came the confirmatory echoing rumble of the hollow fuselage as it bounced and bobbed ever more slowly over rutted ground and the control yoke began banging one's shins.

Early one morning, when I sensed I must be near the solo hurdle, we got airborne to find, alas, that an inversion had effectively hidden the airfield. Nevertheless we persisted with regular text-book circuits by timing the straight leg before each 90-degree turn. After four good landings the CFI said, 'Well, you are ready, but obviously I can't let you go in this visibility.'

So, impatiently, I had to await the next weekend, when September slipped into October before the CFI climbed out after three consecutive good circuits. 'Righto, do just one circuit and come in,' he said. As he fastened the safety belts across his empty seat I asked some fatuous technical question in an attempt to present an impression of 'sang froid'; then, fatalistically, I taxied out and turned into wind. Ten minutes later I had returned Taylorcraft Plus D, G-AHAF, safely to the tarmac and it was all over. It was late afternoon. No-one seemed to be about and the bar was closed, so with a sense of anti-climax, although elated, I climbed on to my trusty Norton CSI and rode home to tea, during which I was able to announce, casually, that I had been solo.

The following weekend I did two landings with George Lovell before he sent me off to get in some practice away from the circuit. So, alone in the air for only the second time, I headed towards Salisbury. After a time I turned but could not at once see High Post and spent some anxious minutes until the winding Avon led me back.

Autumn is a beautiful time to fly and the golden yellows, coppers, russets and reds of the dying leaves in scattered wood or secluded spinney lent enchantment to the aerial view of the Plain as I wheeled, swooped and soared in the splendour of my newly-discovered kingdom. 'What was that? Could it be another aeroplane dangerously close?' I glanced up as a shadow flickered across my eyes and then laughed at my foolishness for it had been cast by the steel-tube cabin framing of my own aircraft as it changed headings. I amused myself for a while by circling, absorbed in those hallucinatory revolving bars of the ever-moving cage thrown around me by the low autumnal sun.

Or I could circle at will near Amesbury over the age-old mystery of those huge upright stones with their incredibly-balanced giant lintels. Who put them there, when and how? Had I not read somewhere that the early aviators were superstitious and considered it an ill-omen to fly over them? I thought, with a shudder, of the roadside stone cross to the memory of Captain Lorraine and Staff Sergeant Wilson a thousand feet beneath my wings. Stonehenge slipped away behind as I turned south where the slender finger of Salisbury's cathedral spire has beckoned for over seven hundred years.

Soon it was time to take the test for a private pilot's 'A' licence for only three hours solo were required and no cross-country experience. The flying test consisted of taking off, climbing to 800 feet and flying five figure-of-eight turns round two fixed points on the ground, such as a prominent tree and the hangars, without losing or gaining height. This was followed by a further climb to 2,000 feet where the throttle was closed and a gliding approach made to a landing. As the test was flown solo, being merely observed from the ground, a barograph was installed behind the pilot; this produced an ink chart to show any deviation from the required flight path. Although stretching the glide by unauthorised use of the engine could cause a hiccup in the straight line descent graph, it was advised that a prudent engine-warming burst of power be applied in the course of normal good airmanship.

I flew the test on 12 January, 1947, my last flight from High Post, was catechised by Sqn Ldr Doran-Webb and, with a grand total of 20 hours and 55 minutes flying time in my log book, I became certificated aviator No. 22302. I had joined the international freemasonry of licensed pilots.

The end of the war saw a surfeit of Spitfires and a decrease in the demand for draughtsmen despite the burgeoning jets. The dictates of a diversification policy sent me to London in contact with the film industry. It happened this way.

In 1946, David Rawnsley, head of the Rank Organisation's Research Department, carried out an investigation into studio methods and concluded that the use of vast sound stages was wasteful. It was considered that greater speed and economy could be achieved by intensified pre-planning, new mobile equipment and increased use of 'Back Projection' (BP). His ideas for mobile equipment were passed to consulting engineer, E. Ramsay Green, for detail designs to be produced. As some of the equipment was to be manufactured by the Supermarine works, I was one of three TDO draughtsmen sent to London 'for a few weeks' to work with the consultant's staff and ensure that drawings would be suited to the company's methods. Two were soon recalled but I stayed on as sole liaison draughtsman and general plenipotentiary for well over two years.

Armed with a new flying licence you are bound to feel a hell of a fellow and, as I commuted each week to London, I wondered if those fellow travellers on the train realised I was a superior being – a pilot. Wrapped in such thoughts, I stared through grimy windows while the rhythmic rattle of

53

the train sped us through Hampshire into Surrey; to me each passing field became a landing place to be carefully considered, accepted or discarded. Could I get into that one? Hmm! The next was tricky with that row of elms at one end and beware of those power lines. Could one side-slip through that gap in the trees? As each likely pasture was snatched away another called for instant fresh judgement until, wearying of the diversion, backward glance into the carriage confirmed that my new-fledged transcendence was being met with overwhelming indifference. Such arrogance was soon tempered by the reflection that perhaps the little man in the bowler sitting opposite had known what it was to sweep low over occupied France or circle high in the hellish flack-strewn night over Hamburg. It was a humbling thought and I felt ashamed.

In the early London days we shared offices behind the Cumberland Hotel with the film people, but later the engineering consultant moved to Broadway. With his half dozen staff I helped to draw the new equipment consisting of combined BP screenholder and light-rail, mobile light-bridges, a hexagonal rotating stage, mobile rostrums for carrying pre-fabricated scenery and screen frames.

Sometimes, foregoing lunch, I rushed across London to a Public Record Library to browse through rare copies of *Jane's All the World's Aircraft*. Wartime shortages still prevailed and hot pub lunches often consisted of oily-tasting whale meat while the appalling flavour of British restaurant cottage pie, snatched en route to Waterloo Station on Fridays, lingers yet. In the evening I often settled for a Joe Lyons meal, sometimes followed by cheery boisterous musicals like the new 'Oklahoma' and 'Annie Get Your Gun', seen from the 'gods'. Other times I brushed up wartime skills at aircraft recognition competitions held in the Royal Aeronautical Society library. Or I journeyed to the Red Barn in a northern suburb where George Webb's Dixielanders played exciting traditional jazz. At station halts, on returning to the city, the late night quiet was pierced by the joyous trills of Wally Fawkes' clarinet, punctuated by a gruff, 'Shurrup' from some unseen Philistine.

Work-associated visits to Pinewood and Denham gave fascinating insight into the film-makers' art. In the studio grounds at Denham, a huge water tank had been erected before a gigantic painted sky backdrop. On the surface of the water floated several models of galleons, each just able to conceal a helmsman within its gun bedecked hull. A network of underwater pipes could release bursts of compressed air to feign the cannon-ball waterspouts of Captain Hornblower's day. I marvelled at the ingenuity but it was the simulation of tempest that shocked. A number of wooden Mosquitos had been literally sawn through just behind the wing and positioned to aim propeller slipstream blast across the water. Scattered about the boggy site, lying on their sides, were spare Rolls Royce engines; Merlins in the mud!

On 22 August, 1946, the weekly journal, *Flight*, published an article by Risteard MacRoibin entitled 'Encouragement for Fools'. Discussing the use

Sport of the Air.

'. . . we could follow Mignet into the air . . .'.

of small simple aeroplanes the writer suggested that 'we could follow Mignet into the skies and, as in his delightful drawing, we could peer over the edge of our own cockpit at our fellow-men below, straining on elastic ropes, and mutter contemptuously to ourselves: ''Que font-ils donc en bas?'' '

The very week I began my aerial apprenticeship at High Post, a man named R. W. Clegg wrote in response to the article proposing the formation of an amateur association to present a united approach to the Government for a revision of stringent Certificate of Airworthiness regulations. Further correspondence led, on 26 October, 1946, to the formation of the Ultra Light Aircraft Association (ULAA) which I joined a few months later.

When I next flew, early in March 1947, the Club had moved permanently to Thruxton. With a new instructor named Axelberg, inevitably distorted to Vauxelberg due to his passion for vintage Vauxhalls, I practised holding the nose up; on the spinning horizon during steep turns, on the steadier horizon during side-slips. In the mesmerism of the latter lay their danger for, with forward speed converted into sideways slip by crossed controls surplus height loss was fast and it never ceased to surprise me how late skilled recovery could be left without wiping the undercarriage off sideways in landing. The novice's usual problem on levelling off was excessive speed caused by allowing the nose to drop in the slip. Sometimes this could be 'killed' by the drag of last minute rudder kicking or swish-tailing. With more experience and an acquired 'feel' for the aeroplane, I later found it possible to lose excess height on an approach by a, cautiously developed, partial stall.

While I was thus beginning to learn about flying, the new Ultra Light Aircraft Association held their first AGM on 12 April, 1947, and elected the first permanent committee which included Ron Clegg, the two Imray brothers and, as Chairman of the Design Sub-Committee, Group Capt E. L. Mole.

As the movement grew, a regular news bulletin was circulated and members banded together locally but the difficulty lay in deciding what types of aeroplane to use; ex-military machines were costly to operate and few economical light aircraft had survived the war. Of the pre-war designs, C. H. Latimer-Needham's 1936 parasol Luton Minor was one of the first to be resurrected, by Arthur Ord-Hume; another was A. R. Weyl's Kitten cantilever low-wing design of 1937; other possibilities embraced the very clean, tiny Chilton monoplane and the Tipsy S.2. By far the most promising among new designs was the Tipsy Junior being energetically pursued in Belgium by E. O. Tips (manager of Avions Fairey) specifically to meet the Association's needs; it first flew on 30 June, 1947. The engine supply position was also gloomy although the Association did manage to buy, with a loan from the Kemsley Trust, the pre-war stock of twenty-four 36 hp two-cylinder JAP engines together with spares.

However, on the brighter side, an agreement was negotiated with the Air Registration Board and the Ministry of Civil Aviation to allow ultra light aircraft (1,000 lbs auw limit) to be operated on a special Permit to Fly basis, permits being issued by the Ministry on the recommendation of the Association. Agreement was also reached to allow aircraft in this category to be homebuilt by members to designs approved by the Association and subject to its supervision. Such concessions were to prove of vital importance to me.

At Thruxton, it was well over a year after gaining my 'A' licence that Bert Hawkins and I clambered up to a dizzy 10,000 feet in the bigger Auster J/1 and, between stalls, steep turns and loops, I was introduced to the dreaded spin. Action in the event of fire was demonstrated and how to restart the engine in the air – very realistically since the propeller actually stopped dead. The aeroplane required a very steep dive and a hefty flick of rudder on the pull-up to get it turning again. Some time after, George Lovell and his elderly pupil were killed in another Auster when it reputedly struck the ground still in the straight steep dive which precedes the spin recovery flare. At the Club it was argued that, if you were unlikely to have enough height to recover fully, it was better to stay in the spin and hit the ground flatter and slower. I think human reactions would always compel you to believe you did have enough height to recover.

In March 1948 an article appeared in *The Aeroplane* headed 'Towards the

J.O.I. and Mrs Gabrielle ('Gabby') Patterson, Elstree, 1949.

Foolproof Aeroplane'. It concerned the little German Zaunkoenig (Wren) parasol monoplane which had been brought to Farnborough as war booty. The designer, Professor Dr Ing H. Winter, had planned 'an aircraft capable of being flown without flying instruction at all after only half an hour's ground instruction'. Whilst the claim had not been proved, the writer did summarise its operation as 'to take off, open the throttle and the aircraft cannot fail to fly itself away' and 'to land, you put the stick comfortably with

Instructors, left to right: Vera Strodl, Gabrielle Patterson, Jean Bird.

Three bell tents at the ULAA camp at Elstree, 1949.

40 mph on the clock and wait until the ground hits the aircraft'. It sounded ideal for, and was purchased by, the ULAA in 1949.

By the summer of 1948 a second Tipsy Junior had been completed and both examples were flown from Belgium to White Waltham for demonstration. So impressive were they that one remained in this country, was bought by Fairey and registered G-AMVP.

In pursuit of its declared aims to promote the well-being of sport flying, the ULAA organised a summer training camp in conjunction with the Women's Junior Air Corps at Elstree in 1949. I was one of a mixed group, about a dozen strong, who lived in bell-tents pitched on the airfield. Two Piper Cub J.3s were hired from Wing Cmdr O. V. (Titch) Holmes. Ground school lectures were given in the open air and, in the main, we made our own entertainment. The instructors were all ex-wartime ATA women ferry pilots led by Mrs Gabrielle (Gabby) Patterson, an intelligent woman of high integrity. In my schooldays I had read her article on air racing in *Popular Flying* when she had been a 'seven day wonder', as she described herself to me, because she was the first woman appointed to the GAPAN panel of examiners and the first to receive an instructor's certificate. She told me how, in her early days, she was forced to apply for flying jobs with carefully written, sex-concealing letters.

Jean Lennox Bird with her dark sunglasses and upswept hair was the other outstanding personality. She and her father, Col L. G. Bird, had obtained 'A' licences with the pre-war Hampshire Aeroplane Club in 1930. Although an excellent pilot with a sense of fun, she talked to me of the possibility of drawing plans and building an aeroplane like the Zaunkoenig, something she dearly wanted to do. Sadly, her destiny was to die in an Aerovan when an engine failed on take-off at Manchester. The third

Home from the Shoreham 'raid'. Bert Hawkins with trophy, Stewart Keith Jopp in skullcap, Gerald Forsaith in waistcoat.

instructor was blonde Vera Strodl who was very popular with the WJAC girls.

One morning I set off on a cross-country flight from Elstree to visit my Club at Thruxton. I flew from the rear seat of the tandem Cub; in front Jean relaxed, pulling up her trouser legs to tan her knees in the warm July sunshine. I correctly maintained the pre-calculated compass heading to Basingstoke where concentration weakened and, with no comment from the front seat, I cheated by seeking an easier route. Inevitably, in due course, 'What town is that?' she said. Expectantly, I studied the buildings below. 'It should be Andover', I replied, desperately searching my mind with increasing dismay to remember precisely where the cathedral was in that town. 'Oh, my gosh! Surely it must be Winchester,' I added, quickly jerking the stick over and kicking on right rudder as if, by instant correction the mistake might not be noticed. 'Watch out!' said Jean over her shoulder taking a quick grab at the stick. An RAF Oxford slipped past below on a con-verging course. I had fallen into the age-old iron-beam trap and followed the wrong railway line. Thoroughly annoyed at myself, my arrival at Thruxton for coffee was less than triumphant and I flew back to camp in despondent mood.

Then, back at work, when the drawings for the mobile film equipment were complete, I returned to the Supermarine fold at Hursley Park where I was placed in charge of a small drawing office to initiate further equipment direct with the Rank Organisation. After some months, abruptly, the bottom fell out of the film industry, the work was stopped overnight and I was sent to start up a modest jig and tool design office, in the recently rebuilt Itchen Works factory.

Piper Cub at Redhill, 1950.

Quite soon the spare manufacturing capacity brought an interesting task. Our lords and masters, Vickers Armstrongs Weybridge Division, had built the Viscount 609 airliner; it was too small. Consequently a new stretched version was being designed, known as the Viscount 700 and Supermarine were given the job of building it, the wings at Itchen Works, the fuselage at South Marston. 'Crumbs from a rich man's table,' said my boss.

In the evenings, at age 29, belatedly I returned to the University College, Southampton, to continue for 3½ years the technical studies which the war had halted.

In May 1950 we 'raided' Shoreham. It was a lunch patrol, the object being to arrive without being intercepted by defending aircraft. The Club put up half a dozen aeroplanes supported by private owners, Capt Spencer Smith ('Sprocket') in a Magister and Gerald Forsaith in a Moth Minor; the pilots all agreed to fly in loose 'V' formation.

I shared an Autocrat with the legendary Stewart Keith Jopp, his flying enthusiasm quite undeterred by the loss of his left hand in 1917 and an eye in 1918. This veteran coached me in the art of formation flying as our great gaggle of assorted aeroplanes flew towards Sussex. Some miles west of Shoreham, Bert Hawkins led his 'squadron' a mile out over the water (to

'I shared an Autocrat (G-AGVP) with Keith Jopp'.

'Gabby' Patterson's class at Redhill, 1950.

A. R. Weyl's Dart Kitten with W. G. A. Harrison in the cockpit.

Stewart's disquiet) so that when we made our individual attacks, unexpectedly from seaward, we might catch the defence unawares.

Disdaining maps or compass, Keith Jopp navigated our return by simply keeping the sinking sun in the same position on the windscreen: but this old-timer must have known England like the back of his one good hand. We made brief diversion near Arundel to beat-up a cricket match at a boys school where he had taught. Once the irrepressible K.J. flew a circuit at Thruxton in an Auster, allegedly without touching the stick, controlling the aircraft entirely by tail trim-tab.

The bell tents which housed the ULAA cum WJAC summer camp of 1950 were pitched on Redhill airfield. Again the planned navigational strategy for cross-country flights, known as dead reckoning, was taught by Mrs Patterson. Again we carried out our modest little hops furnished only with map, Dalton computer, compass and watch for, without radio, there could never be aid from the ground; each solo cross-country became a little personal adventure reflecting the greater freedom of action of the times.

Designer A. R. Weyl arrived with his Dart Kitten having got lost and landed at an RAF station en route. Jean Bird gave us rides in her Moth Minor and we rode in *Flight* magazine's Gemini.

Ace among the girls was Anthea Williams, first winner of a WJAC flying scholarship. Undershooting when landing, she acted correctly and did not try to stretch the glide when the engine failed to respond due to carburettor icing; the Cub stood on its nose in the notorious sewage farm on the edge of the airfield. Gallantly we ran to the rescue, desperately trying to place our feet on the safe firm strips of that noxious ground. At the end of the holiday she flew me back to Eastleigh in a Cub, with my suitcase wedged in behind. In the air I noticed that the aileron cable guide, freed from its clip at the lower end of the rear lift strut, was vibrating up the cable in the airflow. It occurred to me that it might jam the cable where it changed direction round a pulley to enter the wing: we debated this for a time before prudently landing at a passing airfield to secure it.

At Thruxton, in the autumn, I had my first taste of Tiger Moth flying, under the guidance of part-time instructor Jennings, when from 2,000 feet we witnessed the rare sight of a full squadron of Spitfires circling Middle Wallop. I did not then know that my next flight would be at the Hampshire Aeroplane Club which was much nearer my home.

But I had begun to learn a little about flying.

CHAPTER 4

THE HAMPSHIRE AEROPLANE CLUB (1951–1955)

A turn into Southampton Airport from Wide Lane led into Chevalier Avenue, named after the first Commanding Officer of the large United States naval aircraft assembly and repair depot based there in 1918. The original wooden-trussed hangars still bordered the avenue which stretched behind the control and passenger terminal before reaching a large cream-painted wooden hut; it had been used as the Fleet Air Arm watch office in 1939 before the fighter pool moved to Yeovilton. It was flanked on one side by a spacious steel-framed hangar adjoining the Cierva helicopter factory and on the other by the grass airfield. Above the door in its end appeared the legend, 'Hampshire Aero Club'. For more than a decade this became my second home.

When I arrived on a wintry morning early in 1951, I found CFI Reg Langridge reclining in the instructor's office, chair tilted and his feet on the desk. He greeted my request to be converted to open-cockpit Tiger Moth flying with singular lack of enthusiasm: his rounded jovial face resumed its friendly normality when I added that I did not necessarily wish to fly on that cold day. Like the instructors at Thruxton, he had learnt to fly with the Civil Air Guard before joining the RAF as an instructor on Tiger Moths. He had also served with Bomber Command on Lancasters and then flown on the Berlin Airlift.

Portsmouth defenders, June 1953. Left to right: Turner, Unwin, Boyce, Gould, Isaacs, Hobbs.

So in the fullness of time, like thousands before me, I flew circuits and bumps from the Tiger's rear cockpit. The tired club parachutes, used to pad the bucket seats, did not inspire confidence and I never strapped one on to my backside without recalling the Cagney bush-pilot film in which his associate accidentally pulled the ripcord thereby releasing a month's dirty laundry.

Before take-off the Handley Page leading edge slots had to be freed ready to pop out and channel the airflow over the outer wing as long as possible when approaching the stall; they were locked for aerobatics. The elevator spring loading 'cheese cutter' trim lever had to be set about ⅔ forward, throttle friction nut tightened, mixture control fully aft, fuel, hatches and harness checked. Then with smoothly opened throttle the tail came up to give that exhilarating biplane view ahead, through the tunnel of centre-section, struts and the nose. When speed had built up to a ridiculously low figure one had a curious feeling of gathering together the whole collection of wings, struts and appendages and sweeping it off the ground. The blurred green turf fell away, speed seemed to diminish, but at the port interplane strut, air pressure on the little spring-loaded plate held its pointer steady against the speed-marked quadrant. The virtue of such primitive back-up instrumentation was well proven when a badly-shaken pilot investigated erratic cockpit-dial readings: on disconnecting the pitot-static tube system a whole family of caterpillars fell out. Airborne, the Tiger's rib-arched waves of dope-taut linen and lift-tight wires gave a sense of security as the propeller's flickering disc drew it through the unseen furrows of the circuit. When, from a nicely-judged position of field-reaching certainty, the throttle was closed, the engine roar faded to a muted whimper with intermittent popping and the final glide released the rapturous sigh of

Reg Langridge briefing crews about to fly to the Jersey Rally, 15 May 1954 (Southern Evening Echo).

wind in the wires. Would the landing be a 'daisy cutter' or merely an arrival?

On a summer's evening I accompanied Sid when he flew the Tiger Moth to the edge of the New Forest where manager Bill Gordon lived. Starting our performance with a spin, we soon brought him out on to the lawn, waving energetically with both arms. A later manager complained that, after similar low-level calls, he felt compelled to walk in his lane to prove his innocence to the neighbours. Such low flying visitations have occurred since the beginnings of flight and, likened to the moth and the candle, are intoxicating not because they may be illicit but because only by flying low can an exciting impression of speed be obtained. Youth will always venture and today's irresponsible fool is often tomorrow's respected veteran.

Yet there are occasions when a pilot may have to fly low to navigate safely and it is then that an awareness of the effect of wind, turbulence, aircraft inertia and the features of the terrain must be allied to smooth disciplined flying to survive, as later experience was to show.

In contrast, an Auster was coaxed well above 10,000 feet over the Solent while later, the needs of an amateur photographer inspired a Hornet Moth biplane to similar altitudes which won him superb cloudscape pictures and me practice in gliding turns, sideslips and stalls on the long descent. On short winter Saturdays as dusk spread its chilling blanket of clammy mist across the airfield, the great doors were slid shut and, with the clang of the bolts still ringing through the vast hangar, we happy few would gather in cosy conclave around the club's iron stove, toasting crumpets for tea until it seemed a decent hour to open the bar and tread the rough boards in a game of darts.

In high summer we might rise early to join a dawn patrol for breakfast at Redhill, or maybe lunch at Denham, or perhaps tea at Shoreham. One day, as I left Southampton in a Cirrus-engined Auster to attack Sandown in the Island, a tailwind reduced the flight time to fifteen minutes. During the afternoon's flour-bombing competition the aeroplane was flown low over the airfield while my two passengers, Jim and Len, aimed the missles. Maintaining height with difficulty at almost full throttle, I realised that I had lost power and had better land at once. A cylinder head gasket had failed and, as a consequence, the 'crew' returned to the mainland by foot, bus and steamer which took us five hours. When the engine was dismantled it was found that the cylinder head had started to melt. Another time, joining forces with the flying club at Portsmouth, we reversed roles and helped defend that airfield; despite patrolling my allotted beat, back and forth over the Naval dockyard for 40 minutes, no sign of another aircraft was detected.

As proficiency increased, from a stony beach at Hurst Castle, I would look out over sun-dappled waters to the Island then, past the Needles, to the challenge of the open sea; a Channel crossing would be a real adventure after our modest little hops. 'Fly over in a single-engined aircraft? It would depend on how hungry I was,' said the professionals – but fly they did. Then, in 1954, the dream turned to reality when I took part in the first International Air Rally organised by the Channel Islands Aero Club at Jersey.

As Eastleigh was the nearest customs airfield participants from all parts of the country gathered in our clubhouse where, wearing inflatable waistcoats, we were briefed by our CFI and promised the support of three radio-equipped Service Chipmunks from Middle Wallop. The oversea crossing took 1¼ hours on a cold mid-May weekend with such strong winds that, in Jersey, the reception marquee blew down the night before. We saw no other aircraft on the flight over and I wondered how the Chipmunks could have helped. Sixty aircraft converged on Jersey, representing Britain, Denmark, France, Holland, Belgium and Eire. We stayed in Parkin's newly-opened holiday camp and, as the winds raged, our little HAeC group mutually decided that our father figure, CFI Reg, would never have let us fly in these conditions if he had been there.

But on Monday, already delayed and spurred by the call of duty, we arose to face the elements in turmoil. After circling the field for 20 minutes, vainly trying to rendezvous with the club Hornet, we set course for home. To our surprise, halfway over the Channel, the Hornet Moth appeared and after exchanging hand gestures, it gradually drew ahead and quickly disappeared. Thinking the hazy land on our starboard nose was the Isle of Wight, I made the classic error of deviating from the planned course and edged towards it. It turned out to be the mainland near Chichester for the

Island had slipped past, unseen, to the west. Due to this misjudgment and the strength of the headwind our journey time was 2½ hours; it was just as well that our Auster had a long-range belly tank.

A pre-war member of the Aeroplane Club decided that his two young sons should learn to fly. Displeased at the alleged off-hand treatment they received one day, he bought the Club. Bill Gordon hastily departed and Reg Langridge became General Manager and CFI. The new owner, Henry Stisted, was a bearded, colourful character who ran a local shipyard; he would often appear at the club with a parrot perched on his shoulder. He reduced flying rates and arranged some lavishly-funded social evenings, although I saw little of these since I was studying at the University College.

During his brief reign, the owner acquired the remains of the twin-engined Ibis found locally in a barn. It had been built in 1931 by the great little Bert Hinkler, aided by R. H. Bound and Basil Henderson. Surprisingly, the historic logbook of Hinkler's 1928 pioneer 16-day solo flight to Australia in an Avro Avian was found pushed into one of the wings.

After crashing the Tiger Moth on landing one evening the club owner evidently became disenchanted and, following a period of uncertainty and an obscure transaction, a Mr V. H. Bellamy was found to have acquired the Club and a Flying Fifteen racing yacht; the latter was to provide only the first of several Solent boating adventures in progressively larger craft.

The new managing director called a Special General Meeting on 22 November, 1954, which was attended by 30 members who were told that the club was in debt to the sum of £4,000 and membership stood at 85: our views were sought on how it should be run. A committee was formed, social events planned and Reg Langridge, one of the creditors, agreed to continue for, what turned out to be, another year.

Of the new owner I knew little more than that he had achieved local notoriety by rebuilding a serviceable Gloster Gladiator biplane fighter from two derelicts with the support of his engineer, Douglas (Buck) Taylor, himself RAF trained as one of Trenchard's élite Halton 'brats'. The owner also ran a small operation at the airport known as Flightways Ltd which had pioneered the installation of Gipsy Queen 2s driving constant-speed airscrews in the de Havilland Rapide Mk 4, thereby increasing that venerable biplane's allowable take-off weight and improving its climb, cruise and single-engine performance.

Change was in the air. In the clubhouse a carpet appeared on the floor of the bar beneath the four-bladed propeller secured flat against the ceiling. On the mantelpiece the club clock, set in the hub of a Supermarine Sea Eagle propeller, was joined by framed photographs; one highlighted a white Mercedes in the foreground of a Le Mans sprint start. Another portrayed an exasperated figure in overalls standing on the bow of a civilian Supermarine Walrus, floating on the Niger near Timbuctoo, watched by black-skinned villagers. 'It was just after I dropped the plug spanner in the water,' explained the new owner.

Vivian Bellamy was a tall, clean-shaven Manxman of amiable, carelessly casual, demeanour. A worn Navy blazer, grey flannels, white shirt and Naval tie were de rigueur and there was a constant Labrador in attendance. He was completely independent, totally unorthodox and impetuous with very fast reactions which undoubtedly saved the day more than once. Many were over-awed by his strong will and forcible views which quickly made him a legend but his bark was frequently worse than his bite and ultimately he was to prove a sympathetic listener with a great depth of compassion and, always, an overwhelming generosity. With the natural air of an autocrat, enhanced by his service background, he carried himself as befitted one of the very few Naval officers to endure five years of wartime flying.

He was about a year my senior and although we had similar interests, oh what different lives we had led! In time it was possible to build up a personal dossier on this remarkable man from the historical details which emerged as the tales fell from his own lips.

'In 1940 they made me a fighter instructor because I had 120 hours in my log and had fired the guns of a Spitfire on a practice flight from Aston Down.'

'The Skua was in a shallow dive with the elevators jammed, but with some control from the tail trimmer I decided to ditch near the boat.'

'I felt terribly disorientated sitting there in the middle of the field wearing my midshipman's uniform and watching the Spitfire burn.'

'On the ship morale was low so the CO got into a Corsair to show the boys how easy it was and promptly killed himself.'

Even 40 years after the events, coming from so modest a man ('Not one of the great ones like Bader') the Lt Bellamy stories would sometimes transform our table in a Cornish restaurant into a veritable floorshow as neighbouring diners listened in, spellbound.

The CFI of any flying club is in a most influential position. To the ab initio pupil his every word is gospel and to licensed amateurs the profundity of the experienced professional must always be respected. At the Hampshire Aeroplane Club many were to call him Father behind his back or Sir or the Boss, but, as always, the French have a word for him for if, as the dictionary has it, a man countenances, protects or gives influential support to a person or cause then he deserves the title 'patron'. And he did encourage the art of flying, his sound practical advice guarded us from its dangers and he constantly upheld it.

The hangar doors were never closed; ever willing to talk flying, his emphatic testimony of good airmanship, survival and plain commonsense so penetrated the sub-conscious that his words would later ring in our ears to match the occasion.

'The aeroplane knows how to fly, leave it alone.' (cf. Lt Col Henderson 'Sit still and hold still'.)

'If you must fly low always keep the revs up and if you must do a beat-up never make more than one pass.'

Sometimes pungent advice came while in the air. Rex P . . . recalled an instructional flight beside a relaxed, apple-chewing Patron who reached

Zaunkoenig group. Left to right: Peter Watford, Colin Green, J.O.I., and John Squire (Southern Evening Echo).

over and closed the throttle to simulate engine failure. Dutifully he looked around the cockpit, as taught, to verify that the ignition switches had not been knocked off or the fuel cock closed. Suddenly a stentorian voice bellowed in his ear, 'Well look for the f . . . . . g field.' It is unlikely that he ever again forgot the priorities of engine failure drill, for it is essential to act on the assumption that it will not be possible to restart the engine.

At convivial club evenings the reality of what life was like in a wartime naval squadron was driven home when the Patron explained that, of the dozen members then in the bar, perhaps in two weeks' time only five would have still been alive. And we learnt of that all-pervading fear which could so engulf a man that it took every vestige of willpower to win mastery over a shaking body and open the throttle to take off from a carrier's pitching deck. Yet, once airborne, a kind of peace returned and faith was restored; faith in the utterly reliable Pratt and Whitney engines never flagged for, he said, 'They never stopped.' The perils of safely regaining the ship were exemplified too, when he spoke of a deck landing crash followed by fire. He became aware that everyone seemed to be looking at him and suddenly realised he was the nearest to the wreckage and had to try to get the pilot out; afterwards he spent several days in the ship's sick bay being treated for burns.

When I contrasted such precarious existence with that of a Supermarine draughtsman he would respond with all sincerity, 'I can assure you that there was not one of us who would not willingly have changed places with you, given the opportunity.'

When discussion centred on the aeroplanes which interested me so much, it was a first-hand witness who exploded the myth of printed performance figures for they were seldom achieved when related to squadron aircraft. His emphatic judgement of service machines was extended to encompass the strengths and weaknesses of contemporary civil aeroplanes.

The freely-expressed attitudes and views of so seasoned and forthright an extrovert made a considerable impact on amateurs who had never known the true harshness of war flying and led to some changes in outlook and philosophy. Suddenly an eagle had joined our coterie.

Soon after his arrival the little Zaunkoenig was offered for sale by the PFA Ipswich Group who then owned it. The Patron gave immediate practical encouragement when he flew three of us to Cambridge where our offer of £140 was accepted. Allowing John a headstart in the slow ultra-light we followed in the Proctor, flying low the better to spot him above the horizon. He did not appear and back at the club my leg was pulled unmercifully since, as secretary, I had signed a cheque for the missing aeroplane. When it arrived, late in the short winter afternoon, the pilot claimed to have made several field landings with engine problems. Could he have been 'temporarily misplaced' for no airman is ever lost? Colin Green, John Squire, Peter Watford and I quickly formed a PFA Southampton Group to avail ourselves of the petrol tax drawback facility.

That February I made my one and only landing on the hallowed turf of Gosport airfield when three of us arrived to collect naval officer Prescott Deici's newly-acquired open two-seat Tipsy Trainer G-AISA. My job was to ferry back the club Auster which I did, landing in a snow storm.

Inspired, the Club's reconstituted social committee organised film shows of such classics as 'Hell's Angels' and 'Dawn Patrol'. In the large recreational room, parties and dances were arranged and an annual dinner was reinstated. At first, the latter was held on the club premises supported by outside caterers, in contrast to the pre-war magnificence of evening dress gatherings at Southampton's South Western Hotel as revealed in surviving photographs. Out on the airfield, the BEA Islander class Rapides flew the Alderney route until the four-engined Herons of Jersey Airlines took over in 1956; others appeared in the livery of Cambrian Airways. But by far our closest neighbours were the Bristol Freighters of Silver City Airways for the small club aeroplanes shared the huge metal-framed hangar with two of these. Laden with three cars and passengers, these 108 foot span monsters took off at almost 20 tons. When the engineers carried out extended engine runs, on the communal apron, all normal conversation ceased while our wooden hut throbbed to the beat of their powerful twin Hercules.

Engineless, neglected, and coated with a thick layer of dust, Britain's once proud S6A Schneider Trophy racer languished in the far corner of the hangar. Opposite, near the small office which offered temporary sanctuary to the club's hard-pressed Chief Engineer, wingless Proctors, stacked with dismembered Tiger Moths, formed the basis of a heterogeneous collection of derelict aeronautical flotsam making-up an Aladdin's cave of spare parts.

'. . . it was pleasing to have gained fleeting mastery over the monster.'

Proctor 5, G-AIES, a more formal portrait.

With space at a premium, the wings of the Hornet Moth biplane and those of the airworthy Proctors were often folded but, even when spread, weekly practice taught the knack of manoeuvring aeroplanes into and out of the hangar through gaps smaller than their span – a necessary art to avoid that costly collision damage known as 'hangar rash'.

Those with inclination, skill or willingness to learn were encouraged to assist engineers Charlie Gleed and Buck Taylor in their maintenance tasks: with help from volunteers, the challenge of a suddenly unserviceable engine might be met to place a much-needed aeroplane back on the line for the busy weekend. The opportunity to work on the aeroplanes presented a second apprenticeship, a renewal of learning with light aeroplanes replacing the powerful Spitfires of my indentured instruction; further, it rekindled the spirit of cameraderie of the hangar, strengthening the ties between all who toil in the workshops in homage to aviation.

In the hangar lay two Proctors' G-AIES and G-AIET, the latter owned by the Patron's one-time squadron CO, Commander John Dykes. Evolved from the pre-war Vega Gull, the type was regarded by Auster-reared innocents as something rather 'hot'. The Proctor 5 cruised at 135 mph and was the fastest of the post-war four-seaters; it was well over twice the weight of my beloved Auster I; the Gipsy Queen 2 engine gave an additional 120 hp and the wing loading was doubled with consequent increase in landing speed.

I was intrigued by the Patron's assurance that competence on a Proctor would have been sufficient wartime prelude to flying a single-seat Hurricane fighter so I accepted his generous offer of tuition and was soon sweeping in at 75 mph, aiming over the windsock and helicopter-rotor test tower for a landing. From the right hand seat I was firmly requested to please keep to one side of such threshold obstacles 'on account of my wife, my three children, the dog and the cat'. A few days later, when I had soloed, he press-ganged three club members and sent me off to try out full-load handling. We flew around and rumbled in over the crematorium and the Vickers flight shed on to the main grass runway. The Proctor lacked the notorious 'float' of the Auster and I felt that, as long as the engine kept going, there should be no problem. Alas, there was no Hurricane to graduate on to and the Gladiator had been sold; but it was pleasing to have gained fleeting mastery over the monster.

A year later, as passenger in the same aeroplane, I was surprised when the very senior instructor pilot closed the throttle and, correctly, abandoned the take-off when the machine veered to the right. Once a swing has started many people tended to keep the Proctor going in the belief that with another few mph, as the tail came up, it would straighten itself out. This was a fallacy and the swing could continue until the undercarriage was drifted off: in flying you never stop learning and every type of aircraft has its own idiosyncracies to be memorised.

Shortly before my Proctor conversion I flew in one with businessman and friend, Owen Hill, and his attractive wife, Grace, to attend the 9th Rallye Aerien des Vins et Chateaux d'Anjou. Since it was first organised in 1947 by the Aero Club de l'ouest de la France, the original 21 entrants for this annual two-day international entertainment had increased four-fold. The reception airfield at Angers, in the centre of the wine-growing district of the Loire Valley, was about 250 miles distant. The main body of the HAeC party was to accompany us in the Rapide flown by the Patron. As we droned over the 75 miles of sea the vicarious sense of security derived from the sight of that twin-engined biplane on our port quarter changed to consternation and dismay when it stood on a wing, turned smartly back towards England and quickly disappeared. Feeling strangely vulnerable we debated possibilities but it was to be several hours after our 'welcome' picnic on the sunny Angers airfield before, to our intense relief, the rest of the party arrived. With falling oil pressure on one engine, the Patron had had little option but to turn back. Apparently, after some filter fiddling on the ground, pressure had seemingly returned; in the following week the gauge itself was found to be the culprit.

Back at Eastleigh, the Southampton PFA group continued to explore the astonishing slow flying characteristics of their acquisition. Likened to a miniature Fieseler Storch, the Zaunkoenig flew off the ground in about 100 yards at little more than 40 mph, it climbed at 47 mph and cruised at 53 mph at 1,700 rpm, the maximum speed being 87 mph. It had been established at Farnborough, by photographing wool tufts attached to the top of the wing, that it was impossible to stall the aircraft, flaps up or down, engine on or off. It proved a remarkable experience to virtually lie on my back tracking over the main runway, nose high in the air, yet able to maintain lateral control.

J.O.I. at work on the Zaunkoenig (Colin Green).

With the flaps wound down the full 40 degrees, while the ailerons drooped in sympathy, a change of trim required a sustained push force on the stick but an approach could then be made at 40 mph almost in a three point attitude, like a Lysander; a parachute type landing resulted with practically no flare.

Its extraordinary flying qualities were said to be due to the high set tail-plane, outside the downwash from the wing at high incidence, enabling adequate control to be maintained at the stall and avoiding any tendency to dive. It is interesting that a similar configuration became fashionable in the light aeroplane industry in the late 1970s.

Despite the beautiful monocoque-type fuselage, the Zaunkoenig had a poor cruising performance for its power: the 48 miles to Shoreham took me an average hour each way. Referred to as 'something of an aerodynamic adventure', the Zaunkoenig made provision for the tailplane to be designed for a variable-incidence gear to move with the variable-incidence mainplane; this accounted for the inverted 'V' supporting struts for tail and wing. In the event variable-incidence was never fitted.

Never before or since have I flown an aeroplane in which I felt so confident of my ability to put it down safely in the event of engine failure. The sweet-running little Zundapp engine produced by the German motor-cycle firm was a joy in itself; though until we got the right plugs the Patron had his moments. It was an air-cooled inverted ohv four cylinder engine giving 51 hp at 2,350 rpm: single ignition seemed its one weakness. The aeroplane came to us in overall grey with black engine cowling. We decided to brighten it and, at the same time, dismantle it for overhaul which gave an

The Zaunkoenig duly emerged, September 1955.

interesting insight into the constructional features of this unique wooden aircraft. I did not own a car but as I bicycled across Southampton, balancing a tin of paint on the handlebars, I mused that perhaps I had the right priorities like the Patron: his wife complained that he owned three aeroplanes, a car, a boat and a ciné-camera while they still had no stair carpet in the house.

The smart blue and white Zaunkoenig duly emerged with pretentious chequerboard rudder but at the end of the year, then sole owner, I sold it. Perhaps its final compliment should come from the first Englishman who had flown it, at Farnborough, Captain E. M. ('Winkle') Brown, CBE, DSC, AFC, RN: he wrote, 'It was without doubt as near foolproof an aeroplane as there will ever be.'

It has always been notoriously difficult to make aviation pay. Bringing passenger flights to the public at seasonal air displays could supplement a club owner's income although minor mishap, such as a burst tyre, could quickly turn profit into loss. It was not difficult to recruit a few volunteer workers for one-day expeditions, to sell tickets and push 'em in and pull 'em out for the pilot would stay in the cockpit, engines running; an efficient team was important to achieve a quick turn round. HAeC volunteers enjoyed free positioning flights; the manager of a nearby rival club charged his members a fare. Since the displays visited were usually at RAF or FAA airstations such as Little Rissington, Yeovilton or Brawdy we were sometimes privileged to lunch in the officers' mess: also, after a successful day, the Patron's boundless generosity guaranteed dinner at a favoured restaurant in the evening.

A Club line up – Zaunkoenig, Tiger Moth, Magister.

Of various machines used over the years, the Rapide was the chosen instrument for, like the blazer and the Labrador, it was an essential part of the Patron's image. He flew it precisely and well: many a time I sat in the cabin, mesmerised, watching a wing tip flashing over the turf while the opposite one rose high in the air pivotting about it in a steep turn just after lift off. And, as he would so often repeat, only three aeroplanes ever made any money – the Rapide, the JU 52 and the Dakota.

The Patron – rising to speak at a Club dinner (Colin Green).

Zaunkoenig and Bristol Freighter.

Another wartime pilot struggling to make aviation pay with the Miles Aerovan, G-AISF, was fair-haired Johnnie. A happy-go-lucky character he steered his tadpole-like twin to and fro from Eastleigh nonchalantly stubbing out cigarette butts on the wooden structure. For a year or two, possibly apocryphal, tales of his operation were legion. Certainly on a Sunday, having pressed into service Colin Green, with whom I shared many a club aeroplane, he might hop over to Hurn on a speculative joyriding jaunt. Once, after an alleged full-runway consuming take-off he delivered a, presumed, lead-lined coffin to the Continent.

Many charters from pigeon fanciers involved flying crates of these homing-birds to French desinations for release. When a day of atrocious weather perforce kept the laden crates overnight in the hangar, some local dissension arose when a concerned club engineer phoned the RSPCA. Another unfortunate weather delay once caused the pigeons to be freed in France on the one day in the year when anything that flies is legally fair game for sporting guns. On a happier note there was the occasion when, with no weather improvement in sight, the birds had to be released from Eastleigh, the timing being such that many an owner marvelled at the apparent cross-Channel speeds achieved.

It was not easy to make a living with one aeroplane and a breakdown abroad could be disastrous. Then one day, as the news spread, almost unbelieving we walked into the hangar to look at the Aerovan so recently flown back from France. There had been a glue failure and the plywood skins of the tailplane were detached from the structure; Johnnie's luck had held but the ill-fated aeroplane was to kill Jean Bird in 1957.

It is on record that, in May 1919, a bundle of newspapers was dropped into the river Itchen; they were retrieved and on sale in Southampton streets within fifteen minutes. Distribution methods had changed in 1955 and it was our diversion, in late-summer evenings, to fly football editions of the local newspaper to the small grass airfield at Sandown in the Isle of Wight. We took turns each week for the little jaunt was regarded as a free flight 'perk'. It was seldom possible to take a passenger in the Auster or the Hornet Moth since the heavy paper packs were usually piled on to the spare seats.

Club member Lt Prescott Deici.   *Club engineer Charlie Gleed.*

Club member Sid Bassett.

Club member Bert Croucher.

Club member Jim Ward.

Club member Peter Watford (in the Zaunkoenig).

J.O.I. about to take off in the Zaunkoenig.

It was my practice to climb to 1500 feet to cross the few miles of water, then descend across the Island to that seaside resort where a newspaper van would be waiting. On the return, over the Solent, I succumbed to temptation and slanted down to an exciting 30 feet above the waves where lack of stick concentration could spell instant disaster. At this level it was necessary to keep a good lookout for seagulls and to give the crowded ferry steamer a wide berth, ever mindful of the embarrassment of the Blackburn Baffin pilot who hit the French liner *Normandie* over these very waters in 1936.

Threading a clear course around the multifarious small craft which frequent this yachtsman's playground I approached the assorted clutter of beach huts near Titchfield Haven at 100 mph. A cautious turn to port carried me over the upturned faces of scattered bait-diggers on the ebb-tide shingle flats to position the aeroplane a span or two to seaward of those well-known low-lying cliffs where lay the landing meadow of youthful memory. They swept past at wingtip level until the lone Sea House appeared at the Brownwich farm gap where the throttle was pushed wide open and we soared up to the safety of height, turning inland to skirt around Hamble airfield. Then another quick dive took us low over a selected house with a wave to familiar figures in the garden; would the Patron have to walk in the lane this evening? Full power again, clawing back a respectable altitude to arrive over the home field for an innocent circuit and landing. Forty-five minutes solo time in the logbook but one crowded hour . . .

In the club bar, where all were welcome to social evenings, startled new-comers were sometimes pounced upon by the Patron with mock sternness.

Club member Colin Green.

Club member Owen Hill and engineer 'Joe' Currie.

What engine did the Sopwith Camel use? What was the aeroplane in the picture on the wall? By such lighthearted inquisition was he able to evaluate his flock, instil basic knowledge in the interested, cultivate more deep-rooted aeronautical scholarship or, rarely, flatten the pompous.

Of the many he encouraged and helped over the years, he numbered as his successes those who ultimately attained professional pilot status. An early protégé was a qualified aeronautical engineer who, in his progression towards airline pilot, had moved on to the nine-seat twin-engined Rapide biplane which he volunteered to fly, in all weathers, on the army co-op detail for which the club had a contract. The aircraft had to fly at specified times, day or night, to allow army personnel practice in the use of their equipment. Terry had modestly asked the Patron what the Rapide was like in a spin and received a jocular 'I don't know but if you ever find out let me know.' Later, in the club, Terry quietly remarked, 'It seemed an awfully big aeroplane to be spinning.' For once the Patron was speechless.

Meanwhile, in the outside world, I was called back to Hursley Park to take charge of the Ground Equipment section of the main design office.

At the end of the Patron's first year in command he announced that 1050 hours had been flown, Folland Aircraft had formed the first of the subsidised flying groups and the Hampshire Aeroplane Club membership had doubled. The war had wrought social change and that truly diverse membership included businessmen, directors, engineers, surgeons, doctors, teachers, secretaries, shopkeepers, solicitors, customs officers, journalists, motor-traders, speedway riders, professional aircrew, driving instructors, road hauliers and one much loved honest labourer who dug holes for telegraph poles.

All were drawn to that simple wooden hut by their individual needs; some certainly to fly, some to escape their cares, some to drown their sorrows, some for entertainment; all for the warmth of human companionship. But for those with that inner fire it became an aeronautical haven, a refuge for kindred spirits.

CHAPTER 5

INCIDENT (1956)

A staunch disciple of Capt Geoffrey de Havilland, the Patron encouraged the use of the cabin Hornet Moth biplane with its side-by-side seating. The 130 hp Gipsy Major gave it a 105 mph cruise and the large tank promised a range of over 600 miles. Apart from training work, it was popular as a comfortable, stable, touring aeroplane with such well-balanced side areas that it could be turned without the use of rudder. That this dignified biplane of the mid-thirties could also be sprightly was demonstrated the first time I flew in 'KC' when the Patron suddenly pushed the nose down and looped.

In the cabin, a central stick terminated in two branches, one for each occupant. Trim in pitch was controlled by a short pendent lever on the port cabin framing – push for nose down. Directional bias was given by athwartships movement of a small knob below the instrument panel. Beneath this a projecting flat handle would, when depressed, rotate wide-chord, streamlined, undercarriage leg fairings to act as an airbrake and steepen the glide. A ratchet lever for the indifferent Bendix cable brakes was mounted on the upholstered port door; when it was applied, operation of the rudder pedals produced differential wheel braking. Engine throttle and mixture controls were low-set to port, level with the door hinge. Immediately behind the padded seat cushions a 35 gallon petrol tank was surmounted by a large luggage shelf.

Hornet Moth G-ADKC in 1956.

The main landing wheels, placed well forward of the centre of gravity, made it a back-breaking task to lift the tail on to trestles for maintenance; this relative disposition gave a tendency towards ground looping on the roll-out. At first, the prominent arm rest between the seats caused me some landing problems for, as the stick was pulled back, my right elbow moved to the left to clear this obstruction and the involuntarily induced bank could cause the low port wing tip to scrape the ground in embarrassing fashion. The most desirable feature of the fabric-coverd wooden wings was their ability to be folded back from their 32 foot span to 9½ feet to save hangar space.

On 10 June, 1956, I lifted 'KC from the rain-soaked airport to attend the 10th Rallye Aerien des Vins et Chateaux d'Anjou; we were joining the French at play. I shared the Hornet Moth with Paddy, senior instructor at the College of Air Training, Hamble. We had double-checked on the weather with a Silver City Captain, just arrived from France, and decided to go. After crossing a leaden Channel, below cloud, at 700 feet, we made a landfall a mile or two west of track. Lining up again over Cherbourg (Maupertus), we spotted the club Avro 19 carrying the main party; as he overtook us, the Patron's map was blown from the cockpit's open window. Pursuing our independent course through squalls of rain and turbulence, we arrived at Angers after 2 hours 20 minutes flying and parked beneath the trees at the airfield's edge, the only biplane among a growing collection of Norecrins, Austers, Pipers, Proctors, Minicabs, Jodels and a radial engined Fieseler Storch.

Evening festivities began when HAeC member, Alan, became one of several novitiates of the 'chevaliers du sacavin' at a ceremony presided over by robed officials of that ancient order; he took the Rabelaisian oath 'never to drink water if wine was available' and did his best to live up to it. The extended formal dinner, served by girls in traditional costume, took place in a large baronial type hall in the shadow of a preserved early monoplane suspended from the roof; it had been built by a pioneer of the French Aero Club. Sunday saw the guests, five abreast, bouncing up and down in coaches speeding to visit a French cavalry school before lunch.

Back at the airfield, gloom and depression centred around the French weather forecast posted in the hangar; but Paddy was to fly the return leg and reckoned to reach Cherbourg at least. Used to instructing, he chose to fly from the right hand 'passenger' seat. We were airborne by 18.00 hours and half an hour later passed over Laval; then rolling grey tendrils of stratus advanced over the countryside and conditions quickly deteriorated as we flew into the front.

Forced lower and lower, we crept up the Cherbourg peninsula; each small cottage disgorged its curious or fearful occupant to gaze up at the little blue biplane. A misty haze of vapour spread across the meadows and our horizon closed in. Paddy handed over the map, 'Tell me when we pass that railway line.' Anxiously I peered through rain spattered perspex at the blurred ground little more than a 100 feet below, eyes straining not to miss the vital checkpoint.

But even as I watched, thick swirling tentacles of cloud swept over us, enveloped us in their clammy cold embrace, blotting out all vestige of mankind, leaving a chill grey nothingness around us. Isolated in the tiny cabin, I shifted uneasily in my seat for we were totally blind, entirely dependent on the luminous pointers and figures on the black dials before us and, if we were hurtling towards rising ground at 100 mph . . . For an eternity we remained suspended in limbo, then the opaque vapour thinned and rushing treetops materialised against a colourless landscape close below. Paddy turned urgently, desperately striving to retain contact with the world of men; we seemed to be flying over a shallow depression beyond whose boundaries we might again be lost souls. To turn back was unthinkable since we had passed most of the higher ground and the oncoming front had probably swallowed that by now; besides other aircraft might be following in our wake on a collision course. Two minds with but a single thought, 'Time to put her down, time to carry out a forced landing.' This was low flying in earnest; calm judgement, precise turns, experience, all would contribute to survival.

For long minutes we twisted and turned, trapped in our own little universe, as the limited choice of so wretchedly small fields was made, discarded. 'I'll try that one over there.' A terse 'O.K.' 'Blast I've lost it, where was it?' The descending wings of a banked turn hid it and it slipped away for ever. 'How about that one with the horse at one end?' Then, 'No, I'll never make it, the telephone wires are too close.' Finally, 'What about this one with a haystack in the middle and two tall trees at the approach end; they're just wide enough to get between?' 'Right, I'll try it, the surface

'. . . the Hornet Moth was edged backwards along a muddy track . . .'.

looks reasonable. I think we'll get her out all right too. OK keep your eyes on it.'

A long leg away from the field, a flat turn in towards it, airbrakes out to steepen the glide, the Hornet practically stalled low over a very tall tree right in our path. I instinctively recoiled from the reaching branches as Paddy caught her with a little engine; sweeping in between two trees he swiftly leaned across me to pull on a notch or two of brake with the lever on my door. The end of the short field advanced rapidly with yet more trees ahead and we were still not down. A heavy bang as we hit hard, tailwheel first, a frantic snatch to apply full brake, a sideways lurch on the wet grass – had a tyre burst – and we stopped. Thankfully we climbed out. We had come to rest 15 yards short of the boundary hedge in a narrow tree-flanked pasture; the haystack proved to be a tree stump with roots lying to one side; the Hornet Moth was unscratched.

Now what? We were obviously in the heart of the country with not a soul for miles around. Immediately two heads bobbed up from behind a hedge; behind us a very small, ancient van drove into the meadow. Within 15 minutes 50 or 60 people were gathered curiously round the aeroplane while the incessant rain dripped off the trees. We were four kilometres from the little village of Coulouvray Boisbenâtre.

After brief discussion it was decided that I should go to the village to telephone the police. A small galaxy of ruddy-faced farm girls cascaded from the aged van and removed several milk churns to make room for l'anglais; with some difficulty the motor was started and we moved off along a narrow lane to Coulouvray where I was handed over to Monsieur Pihan who ran the local estaminet and a small joinery and possessed a telephone. While awaiting the arrival of the French law I seized the opportunity to allay fears for our safety by phoning Eastleigh. Shortly, a smart Panhard saloon turned up and a gendarme drove me back to the scene where Paddy remained, surrounded by sightseers. We were joined by the area Police Lieutenant, Wilhelm le Guern, who promptly arranged an all night guard for the aeroplane.

At the estaminet, by now a sort of battle GHQ, Monsieur P. fed and wined us and offered beds for the night. As the long evening wore on and we unwound with coffee and Calvados we periodically jumped up to shake

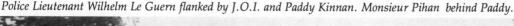

Police Lieutenant Wilhelm Le Guern flanked by J.O.I. and Paddy Kinnan. Monsieur Pihan behind Paddy.

hands with the unending callers, while I became increasingly voluble in atrocious schoolboy French. We had narrowly escaped disaster but, as our host (who spoke no English) reiterated, fortunately it had been a case of 'l'incident pas l'accident'. There was no problem; in the morning Paddy would fly out light while I journeyed the 15 miles to Avranches airfield by road.

But there was a problem. After breakfast we walked through thick mist and drizzle back to the aircraft, still with a little knot of onlookers and its guardian. Oblivious to the 35 gallon fuel tank behind him, the latter had passed a tranquil night for the cabin floor was littered with Gaulois stubs. The Director of the Avranches Aero Club appeared and, with the aid of a pencil and paper, I explained to Monsieur Lebrun my plan to resolve the dilemma. At the estaminet we sat at the great communal table with our genial host's six carpenters while Madame P. served lunch before we returned to 'our' field. Here it was the work of seconds to hinge forward on to the upper wing a small portion of the inboard trailing edge, unclip, swing down and secure the front spar stays from their housings snug under the top wing roots, unfasten the leather straps to pull out the bent-bar wing attachment pins and let the wings swing gently aft to be locked alongside the fuselage by the little pin on the lower longeron. Willing hands hoisted the tail up on to the tailboard of Monsieur P's old open truck where it was chocked and secured by rope. With friendly gendarmes and unlimited helpers pulling up gate posts and lopping off small branches of trees, the Hornet Moth was edged backwards along a muddy track into the lane.

At this point I remembered my camera and asked the Police Lieutenant if he would mind a few pictures: the effect was electric. One of the gendarmes whipped out an exposure meter, moved back the crowd, set up the camera and paced out the distance with military precision as we posed around the truck. After this delightful interlude the Lieutenant gathered together the local country folk: they stood in their wooden clogs in the pouring rain and, while one of their number stood by the roadside relieving himself with French unconcern, the Lieutenant made an impromptu speech on Anglo-French relations explaining, to Paddy's embarrassment, that it was only due to the great skill of the 'chef pilote' that they had all been preserved. A little cortège set off down the lane led by a police van in which we rode with the Lieutenant, followed by the small truck towing the Hornet tail-first on its own mainwheels; next came a police Panhard and finally Monsieur Lebrun's Renault. Soon, on a slight descent, we found the track blocked by a lorry parked outside a farm. Amidst much shouting and hooting to get it moved quickly, the truck with the Hornet in tow rolled gently into the back of our police van; the gendarme driver swore explicitly and we all climbed out to survey the dented bumper.

With an increased escort of two police motorcyclists, one on a Royal Enfield, we arrived at the airfield of Avranches. 'There', said Monsieur Lebrun, pointing to a misty void beyond the sheep covered meadow, 'is Mont-Saint-Michel'.

J.O.I. and V.H.B. in the Spitfire.

A short session with customs, drinks all round, and the party broke up. Although we were short of ready money, I tried to reimburse Monsieur P., our host for the past 24 hours; but he would not hear of it for he laughed and said, 'Pour le sport'. So Paddy and I spent an evening at the Hotel de France et Londres where we were told the weather had been bad for eight days. Next morning, with Mont-Saint-Michel visible, we spread our wings, took off, carefully avoiding the sheep and hugged the coast to Cherbourg where we landed to find a club Proctor and crew who had been there, weatherbound, for three days.

Seven or eight years went by before I drove my VW into the little village. Monsieur P. was tending his petrol pump outside the estaminet; he recognised me instantly. From that day on, pleasant two-way family interchanges took place. But fate was to offer more than French friendship in 1956.

The prototype two-seat Spitfire trainer lay dormant in the firm's hangar at Chilbolton among the experimental jets. I know not how the Patron charmed it out of managing director S. P. Woodley (my boss) who agreed to present it to the club. It had not flown for two years and some work had to be carried out before it was ready for flight. During the period of excited anticipation the Patron asked me if I wished to accompany him on the collection flight. I quickly accepted for, hitherto, I had always believed such an experience beyond the realms of possibility.

As I approached the Aeroplane Club one morning I was enthralled to find facing me that sensually-rounded, burnished radiator behind two huge headlamps astride a jutting supercharger. The British racing-green open body, its ridiculously small doors, leather straps securing louvred bonnet, enormous wire-spoked wheels with 'knock off' hub caps; all brought to life the picture in the bar – recalling Birkin's tremendous battle with Caracciola's white Mercedes in 1930. It was one of the Hon. Dorothy Paget-Birkin team cars which the Patron had borrowed from ex-Naval pilot, Tristam Winstanley. In this delectable Bentley, three up, we reached 110 mph, arrived at Vickers Chilbolton airfield to look our gift horse in the mouth and returned under the famed bridge near Winchester; passing beneath it a wartime Canadian pilot shed six feet of his Tomahawk's wingtip; the Patron had been Duty Pilot at nearby Worthy Down when a truck deposited the tip outside the watch office.

Then, on the last afternoon in August, I descended the stone steps from the mansion at Hursley Park and entered the Patron's grey VW; his wife had come to pick me up from work; with momentary qualm I noticed the parachute lying on the back seat. At Chilbolton the light-blue Spitfire stood proudly on the tarmac, a club Proctor alongside. Owen Hill had ferried the pilot over and 100 octane fuel was being siphoned from the Proctor's port wing for the transfusion which would bring life to the Merlin; the resident jets used only kerosene.

I stood around listening to the small talk and wondering what I had let myself in for. On the Patron's own admission he had not flown a Spitfire for 11 years: the reaction of a Naval Lt Cmdr pilot, to whom I had mentioned this fact, had not been reassuring. Presently the unmistakable sound of a Merlin burst into my thoughts as engine runs were carried out.

I clambered up on to the root of the port wing and stretched my right leg aft, reaching up awkwardly to get a foot over the rear cockpit-sill which lay behind the wing trailing edge; the smoothly rounded fuselage was devoid of footholes. I lowered myself on to the seat parachute and was firmly strapped in. A second helmet with intercommunication had failed to materialise so I was to be denied a calm reassuring voice from the front cockpit and would be left in peace with my thoughts; the pilot had radio contact with flying control. Arthur Luscombe said, 'Wind the hood back when the throttle is closed or you will be asphyxiated with carbon monoxide fumes' – a cheering thought. There also appeared to be some doubt as to whether the hood would stay shut and I was advised to hang on to the cranked handle which wound it fore and aft.

The little group of workers and well-wishers stood clear. Electrical energy flowed through the umbilical cord linking the trolley-acc starter to the Spitfire's fuselage socket. Slowly, the four-bladed propeller started to inch round, hesitantly, until suddenly it took hold; a puff of black exhaust smoke was spat back into the slipstream and a crescendo of sound assailed the ears while the aircraft pulsated to the vibrant melody of 1650 horsepower. Delicately, on its narrow track undercarriage, the dainty Spitfire picked its way out to the runway intersection while I glanced warily around the cockpit. A missing instrument on the rear panel left a three-inch hole through which I could see the back of the pilot's head. To a hiss of compressed air from the brakes we stopped; I wound my hood forward, tugged yet again at harness straps; we turned into wind.

The intensity of sound increased decisively; a slightly snaky run forward as a torque-induced tendency to veer left was corrected, then complete submission to irresistible forces, the invisible hand of acceleration pushing hard on my back, the runway falling away, our nose up in a climbing attitude.

The silence came on me like a thunderclap; incredibly, unbelievably, the

Merlin had stopped. Instantly the nose lowered and the Spitfire came slanting down straight ahead. Immediate reaction was fury at having allowed myself to get mixed up with this crazy character anyway. Parachute? Far too low, and heaven knows when the thing was last repacked. What to do about the hood? I decided to open it and hastily wound the crank. Ahead were small cultivated fields and a line of trees. Chilbolton lay on the eastern bank of the Test valley and the owners of the neatly-ordered patchwork gardens had known crises before, since more than one of the Supermarine test pilots had executed masterly forced landings in the area.

So we were about to make a belly landing – I thought. The Patron had known a Spitfire cut dead on him before, though from 10,000 feet he had easily reached an airfield. Well, all right, as Midshipman RN, he tried to bale out following a glycol fire but the hood jammed so he was unable to open the door: on that occasion he hit the ground standing on the seat trying to hold-off for the flare. My grip tightened on the handle of the open hood.

In moments of stress it is surprising how expressive a small area of a man's head can be; I swear that, through my instrument-hole view, I gained a clear impression of initial surprise, followed by swift action in the front cockpit. Somewhere up front, a cough and a bang preceded a belch of black smoke and the Merlin came on again. The big propeller began to bite and, as it screwed its way through the air, slender wings bore us aloft to the sanctuary of height while the defeated trees slipped past beneath and only the tension remained. The inevitable airman's prayer, 'Please God, let the engine keep going until we can complete the circuit and land.' But what was the fool doing now? For he did not complete the right hand turn on to the approach; instead he was climbing to 1000 feet and setting course across country – with a sick engine!

Puzzled, I nevertheless revelled in the glory of Hampshire's colourful landscape, backcloth to the most elegant blue wing that would ever sustain me. As if from renewed confidence in the Merlin, the port wing dropped, the starboard swung up and the long blue nose swept round greedily gobbling up the horizon in a vertical turn; momentarily everything straightened, then the horizon lurched the other way and again I was ruthlessly rammed into my seat as we turned to starboard while I forced my head upward to look through the hood at the rushing pattern of fields and reorientate myself.

The Spitfire made a wide sweep over Southampton to announce our arrival: from a position of Godlike eminence over my home town I wondered how many hearts would beat faster, roused by the emotive engine note and skyward glance at that distinctive wing form. On the airfield a Dakota pilot was carrying out his lengthy cockpit checks so we flew on over the grass runway towards Eastleigh's railway works and soared to 3000 feet at the touch of a finger. Almost at Basingstoke, it seemed, when the Dakota turned into wind and trundled off; we turned too and tilted down at 270 mph, hurtling towards the grass at a steady green light from

The Spitfire arrives at Eastleigh.

control. Levelling out, we flashed past the Aeroplane Club, Auster, Hornet and Tiger, glimpsed familiar figures waving madly, shot by the control tower and I was punched down into my seat as the nose lifted and we zoomed up, up. I wondered what the Patron was going to do with it but at the top he finished in a vertical turn to port which eased round into the famous Spitfire curved approach because of the blind area straight ahead over the long nose.

Power, was reduced, speed decayed, two little tell-tale doors sprang up near the trailing edge to verify the flaps were down, heat haze trails flowed back from each underwing radiator, I could smell the hot Merlin and hear its crackling backwash as the throttle was closed, quickly I wound my hood back, the 'wheels down' light did not go on in my cockpit. The ASI still showed 100 mph, the flare started, perhaps a little high, the control column twitched, feeling for the ground. Were the wheels really down or would the wings go on sinking, sinking into the grass? The wheels touched, the hollow rumble of a metal fuselage taxying accompanied us to the club house. The Merlin was shut down; the aeroplane was surrounded by small boys. A grinning Patron climbed out, 'Poor John', he shouted.

It was a long evening in the club house as we relived our adventure. The Patron had been as shaken as I had. His first clue had come from the radio when a horrified voice from Chilbolton control tower had said, 'Spitfire, your wheels are still down.' The pilot had reacted fast. The undercarriage position selector and the fuel cock controls were positioned in close proximity in the front cockpit and if the gear was still down then it must mean . . . The fuel was turned on again and the booster pump, switched on for take-off, immediately began urging fuel into the dying engine. I drank yet another toast to booster pumps since, as my French friends would say, it was another case of l'incident pas l'accident.

It seemed fitting that the Spitfire should have returned to the place of its birth. The ghost of its creator was surely with us that evening for amidst the row of beer mugs hanging from the ceiling was that very special one inscribed: HAeC R. J. Mitchell 1st Solo 1.7.34. G-ABEK.

A man arrived at the club, a boilermaker by trade, with no aviation background or flying training. He had built a Flying Flea which the Patron acquired. Then, for half a crown a time, we made fast runs up and down the edge of the airfield. This little craft was so short-coupled it was difficult to keep straight and when we went fast enough for fright, the instinctive response of closing the throttle compounded our cowardice since it had been installed in the early French fashion of 'push to close', the reverse of normal procedure: no-one was brave enough to attempt flight. The builder returned, insistent that he fly it and, unable to dissuade him, reluctantly the Patron sold the aeroplane back. He succeeded in getting off the ground but his dilemma lay in not knowing how to land it and moments later he lay, with bleeding nose, among the wreckage. The happy sequel to his accident came in 1962 when he obtained his pilot's licence after learning to fly with the club.

The Patron had acquired a big, soft, woolly, reliable Avro Nineteen. Previously operated by Railway Air Services, this nine-seater with its side-by-side dual controls was a civil version of the faithful 'Annie' Anson; G-AHIB had been renovated by the club engineer, J. R. Currie.

A month after the Spitfire incident, four of us flew to North Africa on holiday. With only two (non-flyers) in the cabin there was ample room for two bicycles, the front wheels removed for easy stowage. When the two 420 hp Cheetahs were opened up we trundled across the grass, lifted and set a southerly course. The engine-driven hydraulic pump raised the undercarriage at a touch, eliminating the notorious hand-cranking of its Service forebear. The Isle of Wight was obscured by a carpet of cloud as we climbed to 11,000 feet while I was dismayed at the onset of toothache; but it passed. After nearly three hours' flight across invisible France, the Patron thought to descend; we sank into blinding greyness tensely watching for the ground as the altimeter unwound five or six thousand feet. 'I don't think I like this' said the pilot and the engines hauled us up through the gloom to brilliant sunshine again; it occurred to me, uneasily, that we should have to go down eventually. Within half an hour the cloud sheet fragmented as forecast, puffy cloudlets dappled the ground, the silvery reflections of the Gironde lay to starboard and Bordeaux straight ahead. The Patron gave me the landing and talked me down to park close by three Mystère jets of l'Armée de l'Air colourfully mirrored in tarmac rain puddles.

Refuelled, we crossed the menacing mountains of Spain and came to Madrid where we night stopped to get welded a fractured port engine

The HAeC Avro 19 en-route to Tangier (Reg Cherriman).

exhaust collector. Next day, en route with engines synchronised, the pilot left me in charge and retired to the cabin with a firm 'Don't alter anything.' As the inhospitable terrain slipped past, further rising ground ahead caused some concern. Conscious of my brief, regardless of the radio compass, I decided to edge round the peaks. A disconcerted pilot reappeared claiming he had awoken to see mountainsides rushing past the cabin window. My 'diversion' took us over Gibraltar – my first sight of the dramatic cloud-topped Rock. Crossing the narrow blue straits, we came to the sandy beaches, the brilliant white box-buildings, the flowery terraces of mysterious Tangier, then an international zone policed by the Belgians.

High on a hill, we lived in the Villa Miramosa. By day we pedalled our bicycles round the countryside or pushed them to the top of Cap Spartel for espadon (swordfish) steaks or, when emboldened by wine, fried octopus. Sweeping downhill past a group of camels, we heard a curious buzzing and suddenly dashed through a swarm of hornets which bombarded our bodies, causing us to tear off our shirts as we rode; miraculously we escaped unstung. In Tangier, fast smugglers-boats lay innocently in harbour; in the Socco we acquired a taste for mint 'tée arab'; at open-air cafés we bartered for trinkets with street traders; at the French Salon du Tée we gorged our-selves on gateaux. By night we descended from our eyrie on to the town, incongruously immaculate in blazers and ties amongst the dark-skinned, robed throng; aperitifs at Dean's bar, dinner at a French restaurant, once the luxurious El Minzah, drinks at dubious clubs like the Pagoda.

Back home, on a wintry morn, the hard ground bore traces of snow and a treacherous icy crust carpeted the apron in front of the hangar where the Avro was being prepared for flight. In the cockpit, Jimmy Ward initiated starting procedures for the port engine. It failed to start and spat back; a

The Avro 19 at Tangier (Reg Cherriman).

carburettor fire followed with petrol dripping down beneath the engine. On the cry of 'Fire', Jim left the cockpit hastily, emerged from the cabin door, saw the pool of burning fuel on the ground, removed his new cloth cap and proceeded to beat out the flames with it. Meanwhile, the elderly chief engineer stepped gingerly across the slippery apron into the hangar shouting, 'Fire, fire'. High on the wing of a Bristol Freighter, where spar modifications were being riveted, Silver City engineers glanced down at the waving arms, wondering what the 'old fool' was going on about. Treading carefully I followed him and took the fire extinguisher he handed down from the hangar wall as he paused for breath and took a quick pill. Outside Jim had extinquished the ground fire when, glancing up, he noticed for the first time the larger carburettor conflagration above his head. White foam spurted out, removed the danger and brought the comedy to a close.

The Avro served us well; it helped to earn its keep joyriding and it bore club members to Plymouth (Roborough) to bid farewell to a Mayflower replica about to essay the Atlantic crossing. After the party, on a whim, we continued westwards to the Scilly Isles, being disconcerted when the fire engine paced our landing roll; the surprised staff of the tiny airfield at St. Mary's told how the last Anson there had crashlanded and, too big to travel the narrow lanes to the ferry boat, it had been burnt. When ours was finally sold in 1957, a month's staff wages were secure and another Rapide appeared.

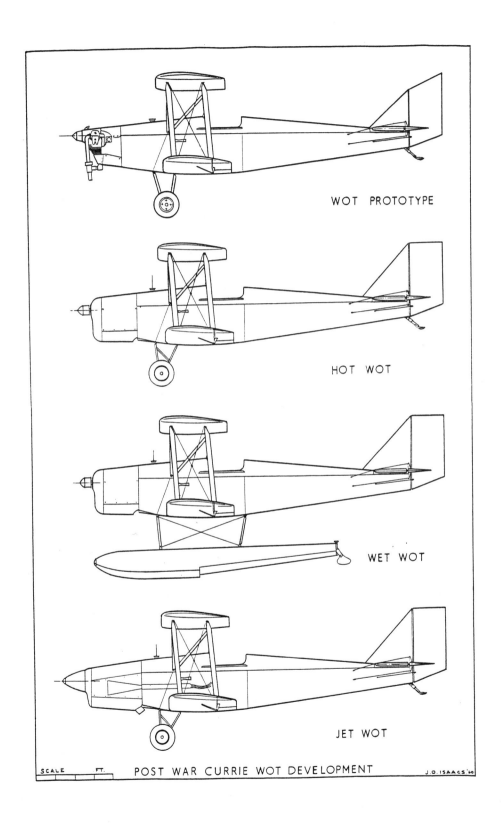

WOT PROTOTYPE

HOT WOT

WET WOT

JET WOT

SCALE   FT.   POST WAR CURRIE WOT DEVELOPMENT   J.O.ISAACS '60

94

CHAPTER 6

THE WOTS (1957–1959)

All winter an ex-RAF Chipmunk trainer lay in the open awaiting a long list of modifications allegedly required to make this seductive beauty safe for civilian flying. When G-AORF was brought up to standard I was sent off solo, in a wind gusting up to 30 knots, to begin a long love affair with the type.

Alongside the club-house a patch of grass, trimmed short, was grandiosely called the tennis-court; to my disgust the net was found to be supported by cut-down lift-struts from a Wicko monoplane. The Patron took special interest in all engines. Where it came from I never knew, but a large steam-roller appeared one day and the maestro spent happy hot summer afternoons, naked under a dust-blackened boiler suit borrowed from an ATC cadet, shovelling coal filched beneath his wife's eye from the domestic supply. The plan to roll flat the tennis court was hindered by subsidence problems. The weighty monster was finally extricated and parked for some weeks on the hard apron near the instructors' office,

That summer, my old mentor, Bert Hawkins, joined the staff. A pupil sat in the Chipmunk, engine quietly ticking over, awaiting the veteran. Bert came rushing from the building, clambered hastily into the cockpit, applied

Chipmunk and Spitfire at Eastleigh.

a burst of power and a bootful of rudder which swung the tailplane smartly into contact with the immovable object. Furious, he stopped the engine and climbed out. 'Who put that steam-roller there?' he shouted. Truly the hazards of flying are great. Bert continued to instruct on Chipmunks until he retired at the age of 71.

An aeroplane burning 50 gallons of petrol per hour is not an economical toy but, in time, I was shown the Spitfire's innocuous 65 mph stall as we sank gently over Hamble. Briefly allowed to handle the sensitive controls, I thought I was doing tolerably well until the voice in the front said, 'You are making me feel sick, I have it.' But on the ground, when the battery had been installed on the rear cockpit floor, when the four enormous propeller blades had jerked into life, when the Heywood compressor had built up enough brake pressure, then I could wave away the chocks and, with little bursts of power, proudly taxi past the conglomeration of airport buildings to the airport entrance where the Spitfire would be conspicuously positioned all day as a crowd-puller to entice in weekend joyriders.

The Spitfire flew in a number of air races. For the 1959 London–Paris race, Billy Butlin occupied the passenger seat. When his publicity team first moved in to Eastleigh the Patron recoiled in horror, steadfastly refusing to paint 'The Busy Bee' on those comely cowlings. Perhaps her finest hour came on 2 June 1961 when Vivian Bellamy won the London to Cardiff Air Race at 318 mph.

Bravely, the Patron let me take off the Rapide from Eastleigh. The single pilot's seat in its pointed nose was reached from the passenger cabin via a narrow doorway in the starboard side of the bulkhead: thus there are no two ways about it – you are either flying the Rapide or you are not. Normally, at a safe height the pilot had to evacuate the seat, then lean in to hold the 'spectacle wheel' while the initiate quickly scrambled forward through the pinched opening to resume control; thereafter an instructor could only lean over the tyro's shoulder and offer verbal guidance. Faith in the Gipsy Sixes must have been absolute for the most skilled instructors admitted they could do no more than give a student a fighting chance in the event of one engine failing.

The unimpeded view ahead and to each side was superb. The aeroplane

Chipmunk G-AORF.

handled like a dream and cruised at 140 mph; small wonder it was the Patron's favourite. When he considered a pilot competent, he might allow him to attempt a landing. Two golden rules were hammered into such fortunates. Firstly, never attempt to 'three-point' it (as he sometimes did) for a wing would surely drop unless speeds and heights were exactly right. Secondly, never lower the flaps above 95 mph, as the operating cable would surely break. Committing the latter sin brought threat of evisceration besides splicing in a new cable. The frightening consequences of the first were to be demonstrated once at Eastleigh when a wing tip hit the ground; the aeroplane was coaxed back into the air to complete a careful circuit before petrified Patron, pupil and cabin passenger emerged; subsequent inspection revealed a cracked wing spar.

Like the sea the sky does not rest; each hour, each minute changes the shape, colour and temper of effervescent clouds which dissolve, merge and reform. As I peered over the pilot's shoulder, sombre parapets topped by ragged crenelations massed oppressively round the aeroplane until quite suddenly, as if leaping from a precipice, the Rapide shot into free, untrammelled air, the vaporous banks swept aside, far below sand-bright beaches stretched south to Granville, offshore the Channel Islands stood like sentinels in a peaceful sea; the mood lightened; it was holiday time and we were seven, en route to Tangier.

Leaving its sun-baked airport, we once followed for an hour the sandy beaches of the barren coast which extends, by way of Cap Juby, Villa Cisneros, Port Etienne, for 2000 miles to Dakar. A derelict (USN) aeroplane, spotted at the sea's edge, melted in my mind's eye into an illusory Breguet 14 for the way was haunted by memory of Mermoz and the great epic of 'La Ligne'. But our destination was merely Rabat: on the return I flew the Rapide and was even talked down to a 'wheeler' on Tangier's hard runway.

Home again, in November, I completed and flew a Piper Cub which I had bought, dismantled, from Russell Whyam at Blackpool earlier in the year.

In December I started work on a flying instructor's course. Now it was my turn to learn the skills of matching the talk with the evolutions of the aeroplane. Once, under training with the Patron, we put the Chipmunk into

'I flew my rebuilt Cub' (Colin Green).

a spin from which it seemed reluctant to recover; by mutual consent we shortened the sortie and landed. As John Fairey was also working towards an instructor's rating, we sometimes flew together to practise the vital timing of our 'patter' on each other. I did not finish the course as destiny was about to give me another shove on to my pre-ordained track.

Aviation had given me so much; it was time to put something in.

When 'Joe' Currie was plucked from the benches of Saunders-Roe to become chief engineer at the Hampshire Aeroplane Club he was no longer a young man but he had kept himself up to date and held all the ARB engineering licenses.

Invariably clad in traditional white overalls, with necktie twisted askew, he was a thickset stocky man with short-cut bristly grey hair, thick pebble spectacles and oddly-slurred speech. He did not enjoy good health and, under stress, would often take a pill: indeed, as an engineer officer, he had been invalided out of the RAF in 1942. As he had been a lifelong wanderer in aviation, his varied experiences reached back to his RFC days, first as engineer-fitter and then pilot over the Western Front. Considered to be a cantankerous character, he nevertheless had a good sense of humour.

In time, he was persuaded to dig out his drawings for the two small biplanes he had built while works manager of Cinque Ports Aviation at Lympne in 1937. I got them printed and the first post-war Currie Wot was actually started, under appalling working conditions, by Club members Bill Gough and Ted Tomlinson at New Warren Farm, near Winchester: after many vicissitudes this aeroplane was finally completed by Ted, with Barry Dykes, sixteen years later.

Concurrently, the Patron decided to finance the construction of two Wots while I enthusiastically agreed to give my full spare-time support. Quickly, pre-cut spruce, birch ply, glue and brass brads were ordered from Elliotts of Newbury, furniture makers and sailplane builders. A loaned table-tennis table was hastily repossessed from a local boarding-house where it had entertained resident ATC cadets under flying training.

It provided a working surface for the construction of two fuselage sides.

'Joe' Currie and Vivian Bellamy with the first Currie Wot.

Their shape was cut from ply sheets before spruce longerons and inter-mediate stiffeners were nailed into place while the urea-formaldehyde glue cured. Thus, early in 1958, as the clubhouse rang to an anvil chorus of hammering by enthusiastic volunteers from the usual Friday night gathering, two rear fuselage sides were quickly completed. Alas, both were found to be identical; that is to say they were not 'handed'. One was put aside with cheerful comment that it would do for the second aeroplane and hammering started anew.

Within a week most volunteers had faded and the keenness of the remainder tested when the imminence of a club dance forced the embryonic fuselage from the clubhouse into the cold hangar where work continued over weekends and holidays. To speed up the somewhat leisurely progress club member Bob Salway was enticed to work full-time for a while, between jobs. With no machine tools available, a few small parts, like bushes, had to be farmed out. Welding requirements were met by the willing Jack (Taff) Hatchard, usually readily to hand 'after hours' as he worked at the adjoining helicopter factory.

'Joe' Currie took a paternal interest in proceedings and under his guidance practical workshop tips could be acquired, like his method for putting a joggle in a link plate. A narrow slot was hacksawed in a piece of steel sheet, its thickness equivalent to the required joggle offset. The link plate was dropped into the slot so that the two plates formed a cross, when viewed edge on, before being squeezed flat and parallel in a bench vice: on removal the link had assumed a joggle, allowing it to overlap another plate.

When I was about to glue on a fairly large ply panel 'Joe' stopped me, picked up an old newspaper and insisted on showing me how to make a paper cone into which he tipped a quantity of glue. Squeezing this dispenser as he moved it over the work, a thick bead of glue was rapidly laid along the timber. 'Just like mother ices a cake', he chuckled. On a higher plane, called into his office one lunchtime, I found him browsing through an engineering handbook. He commented on the differing buckling loads for struts depending on whether the formula used was that of Euler, Southwell or Rankine – a curiosity which had often puzzled me.

While, in the hangar, we coped with the complexities of aircraft construction the Patron continued to face the variable fortunes of a flying instructor. Over the Solent he was schooling a staid ground engineer of north-country origin. In the air, the pupil was known to be of somewhat nervous disposition so when an ocean-going liner hove into view nearby, the Patron was undoubtedly startled at the request for a loop over this Queen of the seas. Nevertheless, he obligingly pushed down the nose of the Auster to build up speed, pulled up to invert the aircraft and, when the nose fell again, eased out of the steep recovery dive. When the fledgling had recovered his speech it transpired that his northern accent had merely suggested, 'Let's have a look over the Mary'.

Another treasured day the Patron was instructing a local veterinary surgeon in a Hornet Moth when he decided to demonstrate short-field landing, a useful technique in the course of a precautionary landing. Matching his 'patter' to the motions he explained how it was possible to bring the aeroplane in, just above stalling speed, with the throttle controlling rate of descent. As he was pointing out that there would be no 'roundout' or 'float', owing to the aircraft's already nose-high attitude, it slammed on to the ground and with a sharp crack the ageing plywood parted and splintered where the undercarriage leg joined the wooden fuselage box, close by the upper engine bearer attachment. Looking strangely lopsided and showing its 20 years of hard service, the aeroplane was pushed into the hangar, another job for 'Joe', while with human perverseness we relished a rare opportunity to smile at the maestro's misfortune.

To assist with instruction the Patron always encouraged local likely lads but he was impressed when an applicant wrote from Ireland claiming to have flown Spitfires with the Irish Air Corps. The day Sean Hennessy turned up at the club, in March, I was detailed to go up with him in a Hornet Moth and 'See if he can fly the thing', a request viewed with some diffidence from my humble station as an amateur airman. Sean had the Irish gift of an amiable temperament, was a good instructor and his cheery presence in the club after a day's flying further enlivened the social scene.

For some who worked on the airport the club provided a convenient meeting place after daily toil; among these a staunch supporter was Silver City's chief pilot, George Hogarth. George had been trained as a Halton 'brat', he then flew Kittyhawks in the desert war and now plied between Eastleigh and Cherbourg in Bristol Freighters, commuting from his Southsea home by elderly Morris. With greying hair brushed straight back, he was a sturdy, genial 'Geordie' and I never heard him utter an unkind word about anyone. Sometimes as he landed his Freighter after a long hard day he would lament what he called 'the saddest sight in the world' when

Workhorse – a de Havilland Rapide. Vivian Bellamy operated this one throughout the 1970s at Lands End (V. H. Bellamy).

the lights went out in the Hampshire Aeroplane Club and he knew he would not be able to get a drink.

At Easter, with Ray Hilborne, I flew my rebuilt Cub to attend a motor-race meeting at Goodwood. The following month I flew to New Warren Farm to see progress on Bill Gough's Wot. Sean came with me since he reckoned to know the field we could use. It seemed rather small and as the Cub dropped on to the rutted surface an aft perspex panel cracked. Surprised, the local residents made their way over to us; we had landed in the wrong field.

My own fortunes were on the change. The notorious Defence White Paper of 1957 led to a shrinking aircraft industry and the disappearance of Supermarine as a separate design entity. The wartime headquarters at Hursley Park were to be closed down in 1958. True, I could have stayed on at the South Marston factory employed on non-aviation work, but such prospect held little attraction. In new premises and no longer with pride in our own product, somehow the Supermarine spirit had faded. Mentally searching for an alternative I recalled my own, not too distant, days at the University College and considered that perhaps I could offer something to future apprentices. So, following a London interview in April, my application was accepted to attend a one-year full-time training course as a teacher in Further Education, starting in September.

Meanwhile, further adventures lay in store. On the apron outside the club stood a de Havilland 86A Express Airliner; G-ACZP had been flown from Blackpool that very day. Almost a quarter of a century earlier I had sat on the airport fence and watched it leave for the Jersey beaches on scheduled service as 'Belcroute Bay'. With its sharply-tapered wings the handsome 64½ foot-span biplane resembled an enlarged Rapide but in the nose, ahead of the 16-passenger cabin, side-by-side dual controls foretold a rare opportunity for four-engined piloting experience. To me, it was to prove disappointingly heavy to handle compared to the responsive joy of the Rapide.

A DH 86A Club outing. Left to right: Vivian Bellamy, Owen Hill, Sean Hennessy, John Harrison, Clifford Lovell, Harold Feltham, a bevy of wives, 'Doc' Markham, Tommy Dance.

It carried Hampshire strawberries to Scotland, joyriders at airshows and club members on outings. Early in May we set off for the Isle of Man to view an aeroplane and thence to Dublin to fetch our new flying instructor's wife. For half an hour the big biplane slipped north at 140 mph while the early sunshine faded and rolling banks of cloud began to conceal the countryside. At length, when it was no longer possible to find clear passage, the drone of the four Gipsy Sixes grew in volume, as the Airliner commenced to circle. From the cabin we glimpsed a town below. There was an impression of consultation taking place in the two command seats while the town continued to gyrate beneath us. Word was passed back that we were orbiting Wrexham, wherever that was. Then a decision appeared to have been taken, the aeroplane levelled out and shortly, amidst the watery landscape, a derelict-looking airfield came into view; its perimeter bore stacks of large wooden containers. The Airliner circled and approached for a precautionary landing. After a while a security guard appeared; we were at Sealand, the old RAF packing depot.

With the aeroplane secured for the night, we set off on foot in light drizzle towards Chester until overtaken by a bus, its conductor doubtless perplexed to find a dozen people walking the highway with explanation that they were going to the Isle of Man but would like 12 tickets for Chester please. In exuberant holiday mood we invaded 'The Blossoms' hotel where we spent a memorable night and, it chanced to be my birthday.

Next morning, aided by the battery from an RAF officer's car, the Airliner's four engines were started and, after a solo test circuit, the Patron landed for us to scramble aboard for the sea crossing to the Isle of Man. Airborne again, we finally reached Dublin for a bus ride into town, a draught Guinness, an indifferent lunch and the non-appearance of Sean's wife. Leaving our instructor to seek out his spouse we flew straight home to Hampshire.

At Hursley Park in the rapidly emptying drawing office, dispirited and helpless, I witnessed the extinction of Supermarine as Assistant Chief Designer Eric Cooper and Chief Draughtsman Reg Caunter together worked through piles of original drawings on age-embrittled paper, consigning many to destruction, retaining others. They represented 44 years of design artistry, of toil and effort, of failure and triumph; all were summarily dealt with and dissipated in a few days. Alas, there was no storage space; Hendon, custodian of aviation's historical heritage, lay in the future. It was a calamity which, repeated elsewhere, was to affect me over 20 years later.

Lee-on-Solent was a mere hop from Eastleigh so when that Royal Naval Air Station held an 'open day' the Airliner was lobbed in to earn an honest penny offering joyrides. As duty 'stuffer', those who install and retrieve passengers, I tried to encourage a reluctant lady who had not previously flown by assuring her she would enjoy the experience. It was early in the day and the Airliner had less than a full load when, with all four engines going, it taxied out for take-off. As it swung into wind I saw the inner port propeller stop, despite which and to my surprise, it trundled off down the runway slowly gathering speed, lifted over the road, completed a low circuit and landed. The port wing dipped and the big biplane slewed in a ground-loop to come to rest, lopsided, facing the VIP viewing stand beside the runway. Shaken, I hurried towards the aircraft, passing on the way the returning reluctant lady and her escort; they did not give me a very friendly look.

The Patron had not realised the engine was stopped until committed to take-off, when, without co-pilot to hold the four throttles fully forward, he dare not release the controls to punch the starter button. Consequently, down on power one side, the aircraft swung slightly until, at lift-off, a burst tyre ensued when it hit the heavy anchor chain kept alongside the runway as an emergency aid to retarding hooked jets.

Now I yield to no man in my respect for, and admiration of, the Royal Navy but they were having an 'off day' too. Amidst talk of jacks to deal with the problem, action seemed lacking. It transpired that the necessary equipment was securely locked away, the key held by a civilian who, it being a Saturday, had gone off station. Still, the poor old 86A lay embarrassingly tilted before the grandstand so soon to be filled with the élite. A moment of encouragement came when a very senior officer materialised, arms full of gold braid. 'Get that aeroplane moved!' he stormed. Evidently we were working along the right lines. Uttering pithy private comment, the Patron thought to get 'Buck' Taylor over from Eastleigh – he would soon sort it

The German Multoplan RW3 at Christchurch, August 1958.

out. In time, natural order prevailed and we finished the day flying passengers again.

Twice we flew in Airliner luxury to the Scilly Isles. Resplendent in its new paint scheme of bright yellow-cream wings and upper fuselage with pillar-box red lower fuselage and nacelles, the de Havilland 86A passed over Salcombe, scene of my holiday sailing adventures, and set overseas course for St. Marys. During the last few miles, out of nowhere, a sober-silver British Airways Rapide shot past our port side going the opposite way. An indignant Patron clearly heard its pilot comment over the radio, 'Looks like one of those old LMS railway coaches.' As we touched down on the tiny airfield, bumped and momentarily lifted, I heard the pilot snarl, 'Get down, you bastard'; again the fire-engine paced our landing roll. Choosing to fly home just off the coast at an exciting 50 feet, we flashed past the pier at one holiday resort and clearly saw the pipe fall from a fisherman's mouth into the sea as he gaped in astonishment at the garish monster hurtling past.

My final months passed at South Marston and for the last time I walked between the rows of incomplete Scimitars, bade farewell to friends and left the aircraft industry 21 years after I had first cycled along Hazel Road, Woolston, as a 'handy lad'. They were years well spent.

In August an intriguing little German light two-seater, D-EFUP, arrived in the UK on a sales tour. Learning that it was at Christchurch the Patron spontaneously invited the club engineers to fly over and see it. Half way there, in the Rapide, an ominous smell of burning assailed our nostrils. Such odours in aeroplanes are always guaranteed to make the heart miss a beat, though in late summer they can sometimes be attributed to burning stubble on the ground. In this instance it proved to be the wind driven generator, mounted on the wing leading edge, which had burnt out. We duly examined, and the Patron flew, the Porsche powered RW3 Multoplan, its two tandem seats in a sleek but simple canopied fuselage. The retracting tricycle gear held the tail well off the ground to protect the pusher propeller which was mounted below the tailplane and between fin and rudder. Streamlined fuel tanks were suspended beneath the mid-wing. The cockpit,

The Club's DH 86A at a Royal Aeronautical Society Garden Party.

clear of the noisy battering from the propeller, gave a smooth glider-like ride. It appeared to be an interesting concept though we heard little more of it.

My temporary freedom enabled me to work full-time on the Currie Wot, sometimes late into the evening. The Patron stood watching for a while and said, 'I know it's only a piddling little aeroplane, but it is rather exciting, isn't it?' It was: our first new creation. A 36 hp twin cylinder JAP engine had been installed and it presented rough running problems at attempted full power, the reason for which eluded us. The fuselage sides, extending forward from the main to the engine bulkhead formed a box, open at top and bottom. The fuel tank dropped into the stiffened space between the top longerons; the gap between the bottom longerons was braced by two turnbuckle-tensioned diagonal cables. Only when one of these wires parted, under the jerky banging from the two-cylinder engine, were we finally able to obtain a smooth run at full throttle. Evidently, with the diagonal wires overtaut, the unbalanced forces of the 'pop-bottle' engine set up a vibrational frequency which caused the fuel to froth in the carburettor and starve the engine.

By early September, after seven months' work, the aeroplane was

'Joe' Currie with G-APNT in September 1958.

complete. It was early evening and the Patron had gone home. I telephoned and he agreed to come back; I just had time to dash over and collect 'Joe' Currie. By now it was almost dusk and a fierce rain squall was sweeping in to lash the field. Undeterred, the Patron successfully hopped G-APNT and, climbing out hastily as rain and darkness fell, he missed the footboard and put a foot through the fuselage ply bottom. In the days that followed he continued development test flying, perched high in the cockpit on a seat parachute. Within a week I flew it myself and was soon followed by others of varied experience. Delighted at the rebirth of the 21-year-old design, the Patron envisaged laying down a small batch of six aeroplanes to be sold for £600 apiece. And, was it my imagination or did 'Joe' now walk with a more sprightly step?

With the new beginning came an ending. On 21 September 1958, shortly before my departure to London as a 'mature' student, the four-engined DH 86A Airliner left loaded with club members for a holiday in Tangier. I waved my farewells unaware that I should never see it again. While landing at Madrid, a tyre burst and it swung off the runway. The Spaniards managed to break a wing main-spar while attempting to move the aeroplane and the last survivor of the type had to be abandoned, doomed to rot under alien skies.

But it had been a good £500 worth.

The Proctor, owned by the Patron's one time CO, was much used for jaunts to foreign lands and John and Marjorie Dykes shared their travels with us when, sometimes plagued by projector problems, the show

The engine bearers were empirically stressed. Left to right: John Underwood, Ray Hilborne, Jack Hatchard (welder), lady unknown. J.O.I. holding down port tailplane (Vivian Bellamy).

continued while ever-increasing coils of film snaked across the floor. To improve the aeroplane's take-off and rate of climb, its 210 hp engine was replaced by a 250 hp Gipsy Queen 30-2 which turned G-AIET into the sole Mk 5A built. My minor assistance with the task over the Christmas vacation was rewarded when, with the Patron in command, I occupied the second pilot's seat on full-load tests over the Solent when we reached 10,000 feet in 23½ minutes.

One weekend I sat in the Wot while the propeller was handswung. Before the engine fired, the propeller stopped abruptly – immovable. As one of its retaining bolts had sheared, allowing the headed shank to slip back and jam on the engine crankcase, I was rather pleased it had not happened five minutes later when I would have been in the air. The general limitations of the 'pop-bottle' JAP became irksome and a used 60 hp Walter Mikron II was experimentally installed using cut-down Tiger Moth engine bearers. When bolted to the airframe, the bearers were empirically stressed by four club members sitting on a plank placed across them while two 'anchormen' held down the tail. Without benefit of any cowlings, the aircraft was flown by several of us which confirmed improved performance and gave rise to the description 'Hot Wot'.

Further, with increased power it seemed that a floatplane Wot might be feasible and a pair of plywood floats, to Saunders Roe design, were manufactured at Wessex Shipyards and fitted to the airframe. Then, before any water trials could be made, the Mikron was removed, the JAP reinstalled,

The Currie Wot (Colin Green).

the wheels replaced and the floats stored. G-APNT was sold to Westland's celebrated pilot and writer, Harald Penrose; it became the subject of his delightful book, *Airy Mouse*.

The Patron acquired a twin-engined, wooden Airspeed Consul, G-AIUS, in which we flew to Lasham for glider flights – my first experience of the sport since my crewman days at Portsmouth. The Consul was short-lived since, when flown to Tangier in June, the undercarriage retracted while taxying.

While, still, such aeronautical amusements proliferated a small cloud appeared on the horizon: the Ministry of Transport and Civil Aviation planned to close the airfield in 1961.

The shapely pre-war de Havilland Dragonfly biplane had become a rarity: of the 66 built there were few left because, claimed the Patron, most of them were written-off by swinging on take-off. With sharply-tapered wings the type resembled a smaller, cleaned-up Rapide. When Owen Hill's example had first arrived at Eastleigh from Jersey in the hold of a Bristol Freighter it already had a long history of service in several lands and its reconstruction presented a formidable challenge. Nevertheless, for many months, Bill Bogatto and other engineers had laboured at the task. It was hoped that the installation of Gipsy Major 10 engines driving metal airscrews would further enhance its performance.

When it was finally completed and flown early in the summer a disconcerting tail buffeting showed itself. Owen sought the Patron's advice and five of us clambered aboard to seek out the phenomenon in flight. Seated behind the two pilots in the roomy cabin, I peered warily over my left shoulder at the tailplane, wondering what unseen aerodynamic forces were

Owen Hill's Dragonfly G-ANYK, May 1959.

at play upon it. Thereafter the Patron got me to cut up old Tiger Moth leading edge slats from the scrapheap and screw them on to brackets which I mounted above the lower wing centre section. Different chordwise positions and various slat lengths were tried and flown experimentally to obtain the optimum combination in efforts to smooth out the airflow.

The older aeroplanes were disappearing. For some 14 years the flying clubs had survived on the residue of pre-war and wartime aeroplanes. Now the situation was changing and American tricycle undercarriage types were beginning to dominate the scene. Sadly, even the HAeC, surely one of the last bastions of the old order, finally bowed to the inevitable with the appearance of a Piper Tripacer – a stubby little device with the tailwheel at the front. I viewed it with displeasure, preferring to stay with the gentlemanly Hornet Moth or the lively Chipmunk.

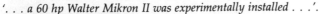

'. . . a 60 hp Walter Mikron II was experimentally installed . . .'.

Eastleigh was often touched by the fleeting passage of modern aeroplanes too. A sleek retractable twin appeared featuring forward thrusting, cantilevered flat nacelles and long slender fuel tanks at each wing tip; it was the latest Cessna 310 newly flown over from the USA. Generously its pilot gave some of us demonstration rides; as much of the cabin was occupied by long-range ferry tanks we went singly. Compared to my Anson and Rapide experiences the performance was a revelation: the initial climb was 1800 fpm, cruise over 200 mph and most astonishing of all was the rate of descent. Although brought up in the belief that the sideslip was the fastest way of losing surplus height, I knew that the practice was not recommended for modern high performance monoplanes so when the pilot asked me to tell him when I reckoned we would 'overshoot', the invitation seemed ridiculous as we were well across the airfield boundary and the altimeter showed 1200 feet. I said, 'You overshot long ago.' Whereupon he closed the throttles with the wide paddle-blade propellers 'discing' in fine pitch and we went down like a lift, easily landing well within the aerodrome.

On the amateur aircraft scene progress was less dramatic. The Ultra Light Aircraft Association had been renamed the Popular Flying Association (PFA) and among the enumerated aeroplane types available to home builders the new generation French Turbulents and Jodels, using VW motorcar engines, had joined the ageing parasol Luton Minors; to the list had now been added the sturdy little biplane Currie Wot of 1937. Appropriately, on 4 July, 1959, the British achieved a measure of independence with the maiden flight of John Taylor's little monoplane which was the first successful new indigenous design.

In the hangar, as ground engineers came and went, I had become acquainted with that doyen of the body, J. R. Brittain, who held the ARB's ABCD and X licences. Bespectacled and with thinning dark hair brushed straight back, 'Brit' was a lively, sociable character. He told me he had been responsible for building the Reid and Sigrist Snargasher of 1939 and he

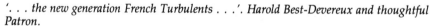

'. . . the new generation French Turbulents . . .'. Harold Best-Devereux and thoughtful Patron.

'. . . using VW motor car engines . . .'. Left to right: Harold Best-Devereux, Owen Hill, the Patron, Bert Croucher (speedway rider).

related with humour many a tale of much earlier days flying with the Col Henderson whose written works had guided my own first efforts at practical flight.

The club engineers were assisted by a small dark-haired apprentice of carelessly casual but likeable nature; Clifford Lovell was ultimately to receive widespread acclaim for his immaculately rebuilt vintage aeroplanes. A pleasantly willing younger apprentice was Graham 'Ginger' Pratt and he was sometimes aided by another keen youngster for it was often said even the apprentices had apprentices as the Patron would always encourage any enthusiastic lad.

That summer, after a disagreement, 'Joe' Currie departed to become Chief Engineer at the Christchurch Club. Throughout all the comings and goings the reliable Douglas Taylor served the Patron during his entire tenure at Eastleigh and with him I once spent an enjoyable day.

The Patron had been granted the pleasure flight concession at Butlin's holiday camp at Pwllheli in North Wales. Here, in temporary residence, with his pilot James Douse, he was operating a Tripacer and a Rapide. When a routine maintenance check became due on the latter it was considered economic to have an engineer inspect the twin-engined aircraft on site. I was asked to fly 'Buck' there to 'sign out' the aircraft.

Thus early on the crisp clear morning of 19 August 1959, when fair stood the wind for Wales, I set off from Eastleigh in Hornet Moth G-ADLY, one time 'Leicestershire Foxhound II'. I made for the Severn estuary, passed over in sight of Steep Holm and Flat Holm, crossed the coast near Cardiff, overflew the steel works, circumnavigated Welsh foothills, skirted Cardigan Bay until, as I struck out directly across Tremadoc Bay to Pwllheli we noticed

'I began to build the wings for the Halcyon'. Note battered Bedford used at Pullheli.

a Royal Air Force Meteor jet on a parallel course. Nearly two hours after take-off we slipped into the farmer's meadow which served as an airfield. On the ground it was thought-provoking to be told that the jet had no-one in it since it was a radio-controlled pilotless drone from the experimental base at Llanbedr. Jim brought the Rapide in for a faultless landing and 'Buck' set to work on it.

That afternoon, his task complete, we steered south into what had now become quite a strong headwind. The Welsh mountains crept past below

The Halcyon fuselage and Ray Hilborne, the designer. At rear the second Wot and the Chipmunk.

until, after an hour when I thought we should have cleared them, yet more ranges appeared. I began to feel a little uneasy since, mindful of the Hornet Moth's generous tank, I had refuelled sparingly at Pwllheli where they wished to retain stocks for pleasure flying. With no sign of the Severn, only a horizon of more unhopeful hills, I was tempted to edge to port in anticipation of striking water. When we did reach it, a little east of track, it was evident that the wind strength was greater than suspected. I debated going in to Thruxton but, looking down at the rotating tank contents gauge behind my right elbow, decided to continue. We landed after nearly three hours in the air, mission satisfactorily accomplished and entirely by dead reckoning.

I went back to Pwllheli several times, once in the Patron's RR Phantom III, and took my turn as a member of the small joyriding team. The flying-field lay a mile or so from the wire-fenced holiday camp and my job was to drive ticket holders between camp and airfield in an aged Bedford shooting-brake. At the end of each long summer day the pilot and I refuelled the aeroplane from 40 gallon drums, carried out minor maintenance, then carefully pushed the Rapide into its tight-fitting shed. Like the holiday-makers, we lived in chalets and enjoyed all facilities but we ate in a staff restaurant. When the Patron was resident he often flew over in the early morning to whip up trade; at least once I saw him loop the big Rapide. Seen from the 'inside', the whole Butlin operation was an entertaining experience for a year or two.

Encouraged by the success of our entry into aeroplane construction the Patron envisaged a small two-seater light twin to be powered by two 65 hp Walter Mikrons; its inspiration was the de Havilland Mosquito. The design was entrusted to my ex-colleague from Vickers Supermarine, R. J. Hilborne, BSc, who, since the demise of the company, was then employed by Handley Page at Reading.

As the early layouts developed, the fuselage became a solid of revolution with seating for four instead of the intended two. The monocoque wooden fuselage was to consist of two layers of diagonally wrapped plywood skins formed by a cold moulding process, the two half shells being butt joined on the vertical axis. To prove the technique a test section was made.

When the complete moulded-ply fuselage arrived at the Airport I cut the cockpit aperture preparatory to the final tricky job of trimming to fit the large perspex canopy. As I sawed through the two 1½ mm overlapping ply strips they seemed rather brittle for there was no balsa core between them as on the much larger Mosquito. Even the 1917 Pfalz DIII fuselages had alternated fabric strips between the veneers to provide stiffening bulk. However, it was expected that the addition of the transverse wooden former rings to attach wings would improve the situation. We also discovered that part of the problem was the builders' failure to adequately sand off, before gluing the glazed surface of the ply which results from its hot press method of manufacture.

In September, as my desired local teaching job did not materialise I

The second HAeC Currie Wot, G-APWT.

accepted some offered part-time teaching and began to build the wings for the new aeroplane which, originally named Hornet, now became known as the Halcyon.

Meanwhile, 'Joe' Currie's departure left me the responsibility for completion of the second Wot biplane. It was to be fitted with the secondhand Walter Mikron II engine we had flown previously and some design changes were incorporated in this first true 'Hot Wot'. To correct the centre of gravity position with this larger, heavier engine the nose was shortened by ten inches, a larger, 11 gallon, fuel tank was installed and fin and rudder area increased. Also, I could not resist building a small fighter-pilot-style headrest. On 18 October 1959 I was allowed to make the first straight hop in G-APWT. Full tests followed and the new aeroplane became a popular mount for club pilots.

The floats, built for the first Wot, were retrieved from storage and their

The Currie Wot on the River Hamble, 29 November 1959.

attachment struts and bracing wires completed. On the fuselage, at the pilot's backrest, each of the four two-piece main longerons was joined by a steel buttstrap. In order to attach the rear float struts the two lower butt-straps had to be replaced by new ones incorporating an additional lug; bolts for securing the straps were fitted with plain nuts locked by peening, an operation calling for vigilance.

The Wot had been flown by a representative of the technical press and when I wandered into the hangar that evening I had noticed the thin ply fuselage decking was split behind the cockpit. It transpired that a small solid steel block, used as a bucking bar for peen locking, had been carelessly left in the fuselage to flop around when the aircraft was flung about. Curiously I had scanned the press report; would there be comment on a strange, unexplained thumping or banging? There had been nary a word; instead the journalistic view was that '. . . its handling characteristics are viceless, as far as I could see, and remarkably pleasant.' Our secret had been safe.

Now the floats were quickly refitted and flotation tests carried out in a canvas tank with the co-operation of the airport fire crew. The wings were then removed from G-APWT to be laid alongside the fuselage on a Baker's Transport lorry on 28 November 1959 for delivery to Bruce Campbell's boat-yard on the Hamble river. Buck Taylor and I drove there to reassemble the aeroplane and, since some minor 'in transit' float damage had been sustained, we found ourselves lying in puddles in the rain gluing on plywood patches by torchlight on the river bank.

Early next morning the tide was in and the Wot almost afloat; it was manhandled alongside a wooden jetty where we had to solve the tricky problem of fending off the delicate wings while the propeller was hand swung to start the engine. The aeroplane handled well in response to the water-rudders but the floats seemed too short; each time the throttle was opened bow waves tended to smother the propeller although fair speeds were achieved. When the fun stopped, out of deference to the aircraft, we all sped down the river in one of the high-speed power boats built at the yard by ex-test pilot Bruce Campbell.

The Patron said he had reckoned to land back on the airfield on the floats if he got off the water, to save further dismantling.

Lessons had been learned and work began on lengthening the floats. The floats had been designed with less than the 100 per cent reserve buoyancy generally required by the Air Ministry for twin float civil aircraft but then, so had all the Schneider Trophy seaplanes.

No further 'Wet Wot' trials were undertaken as another pioneering project took precedence.

Starting the early Rover turbine installed in Currie Wot G-APWT.

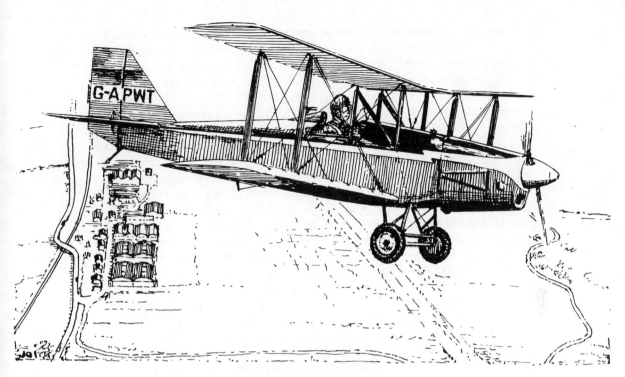

CHAPTER 7

PROJECT (1960–1961)

In January 1960 I began a 21 year full time association as a lecturer with Southampton Technical College, then domiciled in an aged conglomeration of buildings known as the old Workhouse. Here, under the Principal, Frank West, an old RFC man, a generally friendly atmosphere prevailed and several ex-Supermariners were already ensconced. For private study, at the back of a classroom I was allocated a tiny cell just able to contain a table and chair if you left the door open; in the stone floor a concrete patch filling a six inch hole gave evidence of the even more personal nature of its original purpose. In the classrooms, while supposedly imparting a rudimentary knowledge of Workshop Processes and Practice, Mathematics, Science or Engineering Drawing to day release student apprentices, I began to wrestle with every teacher's intrinsic problem of survival in a hostile environment – a problem for which no solution had ever been offered at the training college. At least I was spared the newcomer's notorious bogey of being tabled to teach Bakery Science to non-engineers.

Plotting in more creative pastures, the Patron had given thought to the idea of a practical development of a small gas turbine as prime mover for a light aircraft. A type known as a Budworth had been investigated when, by chance, he learned of a Rover industrial unit seen at an agricultural show driving a water pump. The Rover IS60 was also found to be in use as an aircraft auxiliary power unit (APU) with the Vulcan B2 and the Argosy. As the power output was roughly akin to that of the 60 hp Walter Mikron it seemed an interesting alternative to be allied to the rugged simplicity of Joe Currie's Wot airframe.

He telephoned Rovers, persuasively visited the Solihull factory and a small neat engine arrived at Southampton, lying on the back seat of a car. The Mikron was removed from G-APWT, the turbine aligned and a new set of tubular engine bearers quickly fabricated. An aluminium shield was fitted over the ply-covered fuselage in the vicinity of the side-venting jet efflux pipe. A simple throttle control was mounted, the fuel shut-off cock was spring-loaded to ON and a length of kite cord, looped around the centre-section strut, served to actuate it. With the engine from Rovers came their ebullient installation engineer, Doug Llewellyn, bubbling with enthusiasm.

Then, without a propeller, it proved possible to obtain an astonishingly vibration-free 45,000 rpm from the beautifully-balanced moving parts of the governed turbine. The power output shaft ran at 3,000 rpm, rather fast for a propeller, and this presented a problem because turbine airscrew blades must be effectively at zero angle for starting to allow the compressor assembly to accelerate without stalling. No suitable variable pitch propeller of such large pitch range was available anywhere.

Thus there was no immediate alternative but to try the fixed pitch Fairey Reed metal propeller removed from the four-cylinder Mikron and, to this end, an adaptor was machined to connect it to the turbine output shaft. The turbine lit up but its lack of torque at low speeds resulted in slow acceleration while the jet pipe temperature (JPT) rose quickly until, when its maximum was reached, the automatic control cut off the fuel. In an attempt to increase turbine acceleration the Wot was held down in the slipstream of the Spitfire but always, before self-sustained operation, the JPT control shut down the turbine.

However, the general engine response encouraged acceptance of a calculated risk and, following a Rover fitter's disclosure, the JPT control was discreetly removed and 24 volts were used through the 12 volt starter. Now the unit reached self-sustaining speed and was accelerating towards its maximum when a series of alarming backfiring bangs announced the onset of surge.

Further discussion led to the conclusion that if the aircraft could be got airborne its forward speed would effectively unload the turbine. So with others I found myself pushing back on a wing to restrain the Wot while the engine was restarted and run up to near full speed. Releasing our grip at the command, we saw the little biplane leap off the ground, climb to 500 feet and whistle along smoothly a almost 90 mph. It slanted down for a landing and when the wheels were a foot off the ground the pilot raised a hand, jerked down on the kite cord and the engine stopped. The basic idea was proven.

Engine stoppage on subsequent development flights sometimes precipitated forced landings within the airfield. All spare wooden propellers lying around the club were pressed into service and carved or cropped to try out the latest theories in an attempt to solve the eternal problem of the turbine's inherent lack of torque at low speeds. Finally the turbine went back to Rovers for modification to make it more suitable for aircraft use: the Mikron II was re-installed in the Wot.

Somewhere within me the first stirrings of a desire to build my own aeroplane began to grow. Harold Best-Devereux had told of the expanding Experimental Aircraft Association in the USA and lent me a copy of their magazine, *The Experimenter*. Also I had long been haunted by a picture of the legendary race-pilot, Steve Wittman, kneeling with arms outstretched beneath the high-wing of his tiny 22 foot span Tailwind monoplane: it carried two people in cabin comfort at 160 mph – faster than the Proctor – and all on 90 hp. The British press published an article on the sensational new low-wing Falco. Its 150 hp Lycoming flat-four could propel two people at 214 mph – as fast as my beloved Hawker Fury fighter of 1930. Designed by that Italian master artist, Stelio Frati, it seemed one of the most beautiful aeroplanes I had ever come across. Import restrictions had been relaxed and American and Continental types were beginning to invade the starved UK light aeroplane market.

In January 1960 that exquisite Falco, G-APUO, crashed at Denham when oily rags left in the engine compartment started a fire during take-off. I drove to Denham to view the wreckage in the hope that it might be possible to rebuild the masterpiece. Unhappily, the flowing lines of that elegantly-curved wooden fuselage proved too badly split asunder for my amateur craftsmanship to even contemplate repair. I brought away a tiny piece of fuselage ply, its mirror-like surface finish indistinguishable from aluminium. Twenty years on, its looks still unsurpassed, the Falco plans were marketed for the amateur constructor by an American entrepreneur.

At the Aeroplane Club one evening I found Sean Hennessy in the doorway chatting to an attractive blonde: outside on the airfield stood a four-seat biplane, a Thruxton conversion of the Tiger Moth. Said Sean, 'Why don't you go and fly Sheila's aeroplane?' The owner graciously assented and sat in a back seat with Sean while I flew my first circuit in a Jackaroo. I felt the throttle eased back beneath my left hand as, from the rear pilot's seat, our instructor tactfully hinted the precise moment to reduce power for landing. Carefully I taxied G-APAM back to the clubhouse, quite unaware of her owner's ultimate destiny of flying fame.

Temporarily, our first Wot returned to its birthplace for the substitution of a 55 hp Lycoming in place of the Aeronca JAP engine. I was asked to make the engine cowlings from sheet aluminium. In its revised form G-APNT was a little nose heavy and generally thought disappointing; later, engine power curves showed that 55 hp was only obtained at 3,000 rpm which could not be achieved with the propeller used. Incidentally, this was the first time the two HAeC built Wots ever appeared together on the same airfield.

The two HAeC-built Currie Wots at Eastleigh.

The second, 'Hot Wot', continued to find favour with the humblest amateur and the experienced expert alike. John Underwood, MBE, the Patron's wartime comrade in arms and later a Supermarine test pilot, flew it in the National Air Races. When the engine stopped while he was practising aerobatics John landed in a field of crops at Baddesley just north of Southampton: quickly we removed the wings and towed the aircraft home on its own wheels, backwards, behind a VW. Flt Lt Bert Lane flew a spirited performance in the Lockheed Aerobatic Competitions at Coventry but one of the most startling demonstrations came from that tall, lanky, grey-haired veteran, Adam Fisher, visiting from Christchurch.

His favourite never-to-be-forgotten party piece, following a manoeuvre like an avalanche, left the Wot at a very low altitude, momentarily poised pointing vertically downwards at the watching group on the apron outside the club. Silence would fall: was he in control? Swiftly, self-consciously, individuals edged towards the hangar or the clubhouse seeking shelter during that brief heart-stopping moment. Then the nose would swing up as speed increased, normal flight resumed and Adam would land, having scattered his audience to all points of the compass for, he claimed, 'It never fails to move people.'

Local pilot, short, bald motor trader, Alan Butcher, caused consternation to spectators when he put the Wot into a terminal velocity dive which allegedly took the airspeed indicator needle 'off the clock'. In June, already a chevalier du sacavin, Alan entered the Wot in the annual Anjou wine rally. From Southampton he crossed the 80 miles of sea, arrived at the French coast and found weather conditions so bad that he decided to return. On the long flight back, faced with rough running engine and falling oil pressure, he considered ditching when he chanced upon a small naval vessel but struggled on to reach the Isle of Wight from whence, succumbing to the desire to get home, he arrived over Calshot on the mainland before the engine finally seized due to lack of oil. In the forced landing the under-carriage vees were bent again. I drove over to collect him and next day he set off once more in another hired aircraft.

Sadly, the same month, other headlines read 'Southampton Death of Aviation Personality'. At the age of 62 John Robert Currie had died suddenly in his sleep. But, given a new lease of life, his little biplane (call it Wot you like) was now destined to live on for many years and I had benefited immeasurably from the contact of our paths for the encounter had set me on course as a practical builder of aeroplanes.

In the latter part of the year the turbine reappeared and was again installed in 'WT': both it and the Wot had undergone a metamorphosis. Now, the Rover single-shaft turboprop TP 60/1 gave 70 bhp at take-off at 47,000 rpm. Two lateral air intakes passed air to the single-sided centrifugal compressor which fed the single reverse-flow combustion chamber; from here the efflux escaped through a single-stage turbine. The engine fitted within sleek new cowlings blending into a long graceful spinner, extra reduction gearing had reduced the original 3,000 rpm to 2,440 rpm, a generator was carried, a Varley battery nestled snugly in the aircraft luggage locker, the jet pipe had been rotated to vent beneath the fuselage and – most important of all – a completely automatic variable pitch propeller sprouted from the spinner. The simple system of automatic pitch control for the two wooden airscrew blades, made by Rovers, had presented itself in a flash of inspiration to Doug Llewellyn. The clever mechanism included

Final version of the turbine powered Wot. Sean Hennessy in cockpit talks to ex-Supermarine test pilot John Underwood.

Chilton Monoplane G-AFGI with 55 hp Lycoming engine.

torsion links, balance weights and a torsion bar and it effectively balanced torque against thrust. Although engine installed weight had gone up from the 133 pounds of the IS/60 (or the Mikron) to 235 pounds no structural changes were made to the trouble-free airframe.

Now the Patron could undertake serious development flying and overcome lesser problems as they arose. Forced landings were still a hazard. Once he was compelled to alight on Newbury racecourse; once at the Rover Company's sports ground where, to his consternation, the undercarriage dropped into a concealed ditch, a sheared retaining pin led to the arrest of the propeller and the turbine continued to run, setting the grass on fire around the jet pipe.

Autumn brought a tiny Chilton monoplane to the club for extended overhaul; it revived memories of the prototype seen on the airfield in 1938. One of only four completed, G-AFGI had undergone some modification by previous owners and now the engineers cleaned up its 55 hp Lycoming cowlings and added a long range tank. I never flew the Chilton, originally noted for its astonishing performance on low power, but in October I flew a less demanding Turbulent. The following month a Cessna 150 appeared on loan. The tricycles were coming and this proved to be the first I soloed. By the year's end, the Patron's perseverance on the 'Jet Wot' had resulted in a new level of reliability.

It was my turn. Leather-helmeted, I sat in the familiar cockpit facing the varnished wooden dashboard, now partly hidden by the superimposition of a small metal panel, on its left edge an ignition key, then an ammeter, oil pressure warning light, tachometer and JPT gauge. My left hand closed over the big throttle lever and half opened it. The key was turned to 'ON', momentarily twitched further as in starting a car. Immediately, accompanied by the ticking sound of unseen electrical activity and the whine of a spinning compressor, the propeller began to turn slowly until, at about 5,000 rpm came the characteristic 'Woomph' as ignition began. After rapid acceleration to 20,000 rpm the oil pressure warning light went out. No engine warm-up, no full-power checks, we were ready to go. Chocks away and I gingerly eased the throttle forward. After a moment's delay the revs built up and the Wot moved off, lurching and bobbing over Eastleigh's rough surface. I taxied the brakeless biplane cautiously not wishing to be caught out by the time-lag response of turbines. Faced into wind the lever was pushed smoothly forward and a few seconds later the tiny tachometer was registering an unbelievably large 47,000 rpm of balanced power while the larger gauge on the right indicated an automatically-controlled JPT of around 650°C.

An accelerative push in the back and the Wot swept off the ground to climb rapidly in unaccustomed vibration-free quiet flight: we levelled out at circuit height. For a few minutes, I slipped along to the whistling rush of the wind at 85 mph, enjoying the unique exhilaration; but others were waiting so I slanted down to land. I had flown a jet; ten minutes in the log and another experience.

A few years later, I wrote of these activities in *Sport Aviation* magazine. A kidding American reader responded, 'Imagine the GALL of those British – a jet powered BIPLANE!!' Yet Joe Currie's biplane test-bed had served us well and the turbine sequel was still to come. Eventually, Mikron powered, the historic little biplane was sold to an Elstree group who used it for many years before it went to a new owner in the USA.

Newly arrived from California, an amiable American called Milton Blair appeared at the club. With him he brought his car, a trailer and, dismantled, a tiny all-metal low wing racing aeroplane the like of which we had never seen before. Its 65 square feet area wing spanned a mere 19 feet and its 85 hp Continental swung unorthodox scimitar-shaped propeller blades; its metallic green and cream painted fuselage was embellished with the name 'Ballerina' and the race number five. I recalled that it was one of an exciting trio produced in 1948 by Lockheed test pilot Tony Le Vier and associates; the type was known as the 'Cosmic Wind'.

I helped the owner to re-assemble the aeroplane while American accents extolled its capabilities. However, there seemed no urgent desire to get it into the air. Nearly a week went by and we became increasingly sceptical as

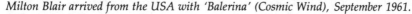

Milton Blair arrived from the USA with 'Balerina' (Cosmic Wind), September 1961.

to the owner's claims. Meanwhile, I tried it on for size. The pilot sat on the cockpit floor, a position from which I found it extremely difficult to extricate myself. Then came the day when Milton Blair pushed it out on to the airfield, started up, taxied out and opened up the engine. Swift as an arrow it accelerated over the grass, shot into the air and flicked over into three rolls straight after take-off. So it was not all American braggadocio! Clearly its performance, said to be 190 mph max, supassed anything seen amongst contemporary British aeroplanes. It was my first sight of that American breed of midget racers.

At the Aeroplane Club several new projects were considered and I sometimes amused myself by drawing rough schemes. One such was for a small biplane twin along the lines of the Dragonfly or Rapide. Such costly endeavour was deferred but the Patron did have a plywood cabin mockup made and it lay in a corner of the clubhouse for a while. Following a particularly hair-raising flight back from Coventry in the Hornet Moth, a club pilot, well-fortified at the bar, was found curled up asleep in it. On a more economically practical level, I was encouraged to investigate a two-seat Wot and a smaller, aerobatic Wot with simplified fuselage and reduced span.

The rather quaint 'perpendicular' impression of the aeroplane stemmed from Joe Currie's near vertical struts and large interplane gap, chosen to facilitate eventual wing folding. As I doodled at my drawing board, adding stagger to give more dashing lines, the idea of a similar sized Hawker Fury came to me. A quick calculation indicated that a 7/10 scale Fury would produce the right sized aeroplane since the original fighter's 30 foot span reduced to 21 feet which compared with the 22 feet of the angular Wot. The near perfect proportions of the plan, featuring rounded tips and a shorter span lower wing diminished the lifting area by an acceptable 16 per cent. In the absence of detailed Fury information, I obtained a set of three-view drawings from the *Aeromodeller* magazine from which I could produce my own outline drawings at the desired scale. A side elevation drawing of the Hawker interceptor superimposed over that of the Wot confirmed how similar the two aeroplanes would be in size, presumably in weight, and therefore in general constructional methods. By good fortune too, little juggling of component positions or areas seemed necessary, subject always to later mathematical confirmation. Excitement grew.

While considering this pleasing prospect, I was approached by a new club member, Dr John Urmston, who had learnt to fly on Jackaroos at Thruxton under the tutorship of Fred Mercer, himself earlier trained by the Patron. His suggestion was that we might jointly build a suitable aeroplane and to this end I borrowed, for study, plans of the French two-seat Condor design. Such partnerships can work but aeroplane builders tend to be individualists so, finally, it was by mutual consent that we decided to each build an aeroplane. However, he kindly offered to initially share with me his workshop space and facilities in exchange for the benefit of my experience and my acceptance of the tedious task of ordering materials; furthermore, by ordering in bulk, some financial economy could ensue. Such an alliance, said John, would be an excellent symbiosis.

Now with a definite project and cheered by the turn of events, I continued with detail design during the winter of 1960–61 while the Doctor settled on a Currie Wot. Both machines had the enormous advantage of needing relatively small space since no wing panel was more than about ten feet long.

Hawker Siddeley Aviation sent me two half full size drawings; one showed the Top Plane Centre Section ribs and the other a Bottom Plane standard rib. Although no ordinates were given, by measuring the prints, it was deduced that the aerofoil was almost certainly RAF 28 of thickness chord ratio 9.75 per cent compared to the 11.7 per cent of the thicker Clark YH used on the Wot. This would mean less depth of spar when it came to strength calculations. Also, I could not help wondering what might be the effect of the interaction of aerofoil-induced air pressures due to the smaller gap between the much more closely-positioned but heavily-staggered wings. Although the five-foot upper mainplane chord exceeded that of the lower planes by two inches, I decided to ignore the scaled difference of 1.4 inches and standardised all ribs at 42 inches to simplify jigging.

By March 1961, the project began with a visit to the courteously helpful Jim Cramp at the old-established furniture-manufacturing firm, Elliotts of Newbury; since they also produced exquisite wooden sail-planes in small quantities we were able to select and reserve a baulk or two of Sitka spruce from their little stack. Twelve or fourteen foot lengths of timber being awkward to transport, Ray Hilborne was cajoled into service for he had a classic Alvis saloon with upward folding seat back and downward folding boot door giving a rear platform support to the baulks which could be rammed far into the innards of the car. The spoils were taken to the joiners-shop of a country-based housebuilder a few miles from Southampton. Here I spent some Saturday evenings helping to push spruce through the circular saw and over the planer. It was like old times for we had done the same thing together to cut spars for the Halcyon twin. There is a ritual to be followed.

First the conference. Shall it be rift-sawn, cut along the radius of the annular rings, or shall it be tangential-sawn, cut at a tangent to the rings? Often the required depth of spar in relation to the dimensions of available timber determines this. The essential long lengths required for wing spars and fuselage longerons must be considered first, to decide on the most economical way of cutting.

It is necessary for a helper to align, steady and support the free end of a long length which may be, perhaps 6″ × 4″ in section, while the man at the sharp end pushes it over the slitting saw table. Halfway through the operation the assistant must hurry to the other side of the table to receive the weight of the oncoming, now divided, baulk. To the uninitiated, the tortured scream of the saw, the torrent of flowing chips, the need not to bend the thin rotating cutting disc nor allow it to overheat, combined with the anxious desire not to ruin the precious material, tend to make the operation a traumatic experience, lightened by sheer joy at the sight of those first vital pieces needed to fulfil a dream. And, until the first cut is made in that dark furry exterior, until the smooth creamy fibrous structure at the heart of the timber is exposed, who knows what hidden defects may lie within? Will the grain inclination be within limits, will there be heart-shake, ring-shake, compression-shake, knots, pitch holes or, that most deadly of disasters, dote disease?

Frankly, the inherent physical hazards associated with wood-working machinery always frighten me. Freddie was a short, agreeable man wearing a hearing aid and he had long borne the common scars of his trade signalled by two missing finger tops. Thus he surprised me one night when, pausing in our work, he disappeared into his adjoining bungalow to return with two glasses and a bottle of whisky. Doubts as to the wisdom of such reckless behaviour were quickly dispelled by anticipatory pleasure and I drank in silent toast to the success of the venture.

From Elliotts we had obtained some sheets of plywood but, unversed in the art of planing scarf-joints by hand, I set about finding some longer 8 ft by 4 ft sheets of 1½ mm thick birch ply with which the 14 foot fuselage length could be achieved with but a single (lap) joint. With ill-concealed impatience we had to await the three month delivery date quoted by a London supplier. Aircraft quality bolts proved equally frustrating. Because they were standardised in 1/10 inch increments of plain length it proved difficult to find one supplier with a wide enough range of stock to meet our varied demands. Steel sheet and steel tube also had to be ordered. As the volume of correspondence grew in the form of queries, quotations, invoices, packing notes, despatch notes and release notes, my 'purchasing department' file thickened.

It is something of a tradition in homebuilt aircraft circles that a small, relatively simple, component be tackled first to gain experience, confidence and act as a morale booster. Not everyone stays the course; it has often been asserted that the country is littered with fins or rudders of unfinished aeroplanes. I hoped not to be adding to the junk pile when I built my own fin and rudder in a small garden shed at home. In contrast to the straight-edged Wot the rounded leading and trailing edges of the Fury's vertical surfaces had to be formed by gluing together several thin strips of spruce held, bent into suitable arcs, by nails hammered into a flat plank on which the required shapes had been drawn. It was necessary to first paint the plank or rub on candle-grease lest the component become permanently attached by surplus glue oozing from the laminates.

When it came to the larger chunks of aeroplane my days began with an eight mile drive to John Urmston's Botley workshop for it was here that our two fuselages were built in close proximity.

John Urmston was a short, balding man of thoughtful mien, but capable of loud, lively enthusiasms, and clearly an individualist. Any misconceptions I might have held from casual acquaintanceship at the

Aeroplane Club were soon dispelled for his own representation as a simple country doctor was quite erroneous. He was one of those infuriating people who are good at pretty well anything they set their hand to and there seemed little to which he had not set his. The large sprawling house where, for a year or so I became a sort of itinerant, middle-aged balding cuckoo, bore evidence of his previous passion for, on strong shelves in the long narrow pantry, he showed me two superbly made examples of the steam-locomotive modeller's art; there is no higher test of engineering skills. In the high-walled garden behind was set out a loop of model railway track for exercising these gems. Leaving the house via the waiting room adjoining the surgery one crossed the cobbled yard to a heterogeneous collection of aged buildings which served as machine shop, assembly shop (for our fuselages) with loft above, and garage. Across the road lay the local pub whose customers, to the Doc's fury, occasionally parked their cars in his private yard.

He was a few years my junior so there was no vast generation gap so to speak and ours was a happy association for, apart from his company and mutual interests, common problems could be discussed, shared and solved. On occasion, I might explain exactly how I had carried out a certain task while he listened carefully in meditation; finally, to my irritation, he would say, 'I'm not going to do it that way', and sometimes perhaps his way was better but, as I have said, building aeroplanes is for the individualist.

The two fuselages were made using a method suited to the confines of a small workroom because the forward portions of about six foot lengths were built first, allowing the rear fuselage sides to be added later. In model aeroplane fashion the ply sides were glued to the short longerons and intermediate uprights, all held in a simple flat wooden jig. To hold ply and spruce together while the glue cured, short brass brads were hammered in, aided by staples interspersed with small brass woodscrews to obtain better clamping purchase; the latter, specified on Joe Currie's drawings, we considered witness to the less reliable pre-war glues. The handed, stiffened ply sides were joined to two prefabricated ply bulkheads of equal width, one at the pilot's back, the other, slight canted, some 4½ feet forward thus leaving 18 inches of flapping ply projecting at the front, later to be pulled in and glued to the narrower engine bulkhead. In effect we now had an easily-distorted box with no top or bottom. Between the two bulkheads the bottom longerons were to be connected by a number of wooden crossties. It was important to guarantee the truth of the box. If the diagonal lengths between any two opposite corners are equal then the box will be rectangular and not merely a parallelogram. To check this I made a long trammel, a form of beam-compass, using a stiff wooden lath with sliding, adjustable, metal points. The top longerons were tied at only one intermediate position to support the bottom edge of the instrument panel. We soon had these handy cockpit box units assembled and resting on trestles. They opened up new areas of interesting work. We could build up the sub-structure and fit the control box with free access before gluing on the ply floor. Nowhere was

Club members outside the hangar doors. Left to right: Vivian Bellamy, J. R. Brittain, 'Chunky' Pointer, Tony Griffin, Graham Pratt, Bob Elliot, Buck Taylor, Joyce Keel, John Fairey, Sean Hennessy, June Slingsby.

more care taken than in marking out and drilling the fuselage sides for wing attachments; only by accurately disciplined work could we ensure that ultimately the wings would attain symmetry and correct incidence. At the bench we made the bent-up sheet steel fittings. At each wing spar position de Havilland practice was followed as each steel attachment was not only bolted to the longeron but port and starboard sides were braced together by long ¼ inch diameter tie-rods to resist tension from aerodynamic lifting forces on the lower wings; reversed, compression, loads were met by a wooden carry-through spar.

On the afternoon of 19 May 1961, while I worked on the fuselage, the Doc was called to the phone. He told me there had been a crash and the Patron had asked him to come and stitch up a gash in instructor Jim Douse's head. I knew that a twin-engined amphibian known as a SCAN 30 (actually a licence-built French version of the Grumman Widgeon) had appeared in the hangar, newly acquired as G-ARIX by Bruce Campbell whose boatyard had hosted our Wet Wot trials. Evidently, on the spur of the moment the Patron had filled it with James Douse, secretary Joyce Keel, engineer J.R. Brittain and, in my absence, Donald Campbell of speed record fame. After taking off from Eastleigh the pilot decided to alight on Southampton Water near Calshot. The landing seemed good, said Jim later, but suddenly the nose seemed to open up as water poured in and the aircraft flipped over upside down. Since they were now under water with the cabin roof the floor, mercifully all the occupants managed to struggle out through the large hole where the nose had been torn off. 'Brit' lost his glasses but apart from Jim's gashed head no injuries of any consequence were sustained. Bruce Campbell soon arrived in one of his power boats to fish them out of the sea.

128

The news spread quickly resulting in a large social gathering that evening. Those as yet unaware of the details looked on aghast as Doug Kirkpatrick walked in for a beer, his neck encased in a large plastercast collar; of course he had not been involved at all but he was known to be flying with the RAF as a V-bomber pilot. Somewhat sheepishly he explained he had fallen off a vaulting horse in the gym. My greatest shock came when the Patron told how he had so very nearly phoned to tell me there was a spare seat going for the flight!

When our eight foot sheets of ply arrived in a large returnable packing-case the rear fuselage sides were made by gluing on longerons and uprights. I thought about how best to join them to the cockpit box. The top longerons being straight from nose to tail (in elevation) it was clearly better to assemble the fuselage inverted and work from this obvious datum.

At home, I rummaged around to find two spirit levels; a short one had come with a small billliard table we once had, the other, about a foot in length and with age-blackened wooden base, had belonged to a carpenter ancestor; by looking down at the glass vial, below the bubble, one could read in copper-plate hand the inscription 'September 1876'. It was a start although I knew at some future time we should need an adjustable clinometer for rigging the aeroplanes. The problem was resolved when John Urmston found and ordered from a London surplus store, two neat little all-metal units bearing the legend 'Clinometer. Vickers .303 in MG MkII 1944'. Although with a total range of movement of only plus or minus 20 degrees from zero it was possible, by reading the barrel markings, to measure angles to within one minute of accuracy. Supplied in a little leather-covered wooden box complete with shoulder sling, it has served on every aeroplane I have worked on since.

As I cast about in the workshop for suitable materials to make a plumb bob to check vertical alignment, I was offered some strong black thread. I thought it ideal but blanched a bit when told it was surgeon's thread. In time I had to overcome my layman's horror of hospitals and terror of the tools of the trade as other medical paraphernalia was called into play such as forceps, tweezers, surgical tape and syringes. Indeed the blend of doctor and engineer extended to John's robust sense of humour as he told me, with great gusto, of the patient who walked into the surgery nursing his hand to explain that he had run a twist drill through his finger. Instantly he had pulled open his desk drawer, enquired 'What size was it?' and picked up a reamer.

As the two rear fuselage sides were now affixed to the forward box, and both of equal length, I reckoned it would only be necessary to pull them in at the tail end and glue them to the spruce sternpost which I did. Woe to the unwary: suspending my plumb-bob it was at once obvious that by no stretch of the imagination could the sternpost be considered parallel to the taut surgeon's thread. Said John, who had not yet fixed his own rear fuselage, 'I thought you were pressing on in rather a carefree manner'. I picked up a saw for the sternpost would have to be cut out and another made.

In the small shed at my own home, I began the less stringent task of making the 39 main and 34 nose ribs for the wings. I first marked out the RAF 28 section on a sheet of aluminium then cut and smoothly filed the aerofoil shape. This master template was dropped on to a blockboard panel and its shape traced round in pencil, the positions of the two spars and all soldier members being added. Nails were hammered in at suitable intervals around the outside contour and at strategic positions within to control the periphery and locate all members making up the Warren girder rib. The nail heads were then cut off and rough ends filed smooth. Although this is a quick way of making jigs, wooden contour-locations are really preferable since the formic acid used with the two-part glue may come into contact with the nails causing unsightly metal stains on the finished rib.

Because of the general similarity in size and weight of the Fury and the proven Wot (although the geometry was quite different) I had proceeded this far with construction and taken a chance on the adequacy of scantling sizes. It was clearly time to regularise the situation. Ray Hilborne had kindly agreed to stress the Fury in his spare time. As a first step, during the summer holidays, we drove to Luton to discuss the type clearance requirements with Eric King, then head of PFA Engineering to which organisation airworthiness of homebuilts was delegated by the Air Registration Board (ARB). Amicable agreement on a stressing programme was quickly reached and we intended to meet the British Civil Airworthiness Requirements (BCAR) aerobatic case of $+ 9G$ and $- 4\frac{1}{2}G$, fully factored. That is to say, the wings would be designed strong enough to withstand six times the weight of the aeroplane multiplied by a safety factor of $1\frac{1}{2}$, in the positive case. Thus from the outset it is necessary to assume what will be the all-up-weight (AUW) of the finished aeroplane. A correct assumption is usually the result of experience and luck. Initial calculations started on the basis of the 750 pounds of the Wot; however, we soon raised our estimate to 800 pounds. When Ray had a free evening, we sat in his caravan office at Winchester and while he did the clever stuff, I checked his calculations on a slide rule, drew up tables for the insertion of figures or wrote up two fair copies of our work, one for the PFA engineering officer.

To aid us in our task, in mid September, following my plea for help, a single dramatic piece of paper arrived from David Robbins of Hawker Siddeley's technical staff. Thereon were typed, from original records, details of the Hawker Fury biplane, aerofoil section RAF 28, characteristics for normal flight at maximum level speed of 285 fps (194 mph), stalling speed of 103 fps (70 mph), forward and back centre of pressure positions, tail loads and nose dive data. Lift and Drag co-efficients of the day used the symbols Kl and Kd which were only half the value of the latterday CL and CD but, as ρ (air density) was then used instead of the later $\frac{1}{2}\rho$ in the basic formulae Lift and Drag values remained unchanged. Further information on the aerodynamics of RAF 28 we took from 'Introduction to Aeronautics', by C. F. Toms, 1947.

In an age of monoplanes it was not easy to find information on biplane

The Spitfire at Eastleigh 1961. On spinner: June Slingsby. On wing, left to right: Unknown, John Fairey, John Habin, Owen Hill, Alan Butcher, Ray Hilborne, 'Mac' Macdonald. Standing, left to right: Unknown, Peter Assinder, J.O.I., Vivian Bellamy, James Douse (Southern Evening Echo).

design without reference to early textbooks. The load distribution between upper and lower wings was taken from *An Introduction to Aeronautical Engineering: Vol.II – Structures*, by J.D. Haddon, 1938, while the crippling loads of spruce streamline struts was dug out of *Handbook of Modern Aeronautics*, by Arthur W. Judge, 1919. Ray Hilborne also had an extensive personal collection of data sheets gathered over many years as the tools of his profession. Thus equipped and starting with the development of the flight envelope we began to labour at loading diagrams, shear force and bending moment diagrams for both top and bottom wings, loads in flying wires, drag loads in wing structures. At critical points, the detail design of fittings was checked and considerable effort went into stressing the centre section by strain energy methods.

Back at the village aircraft factory, most metal fittings had been bolted to the fuselages and the bent thin-ply turtle-back decking applied. Briefly resting from our toil, John once carried one of his locomotive gems into the back garden to raise steam while mentally I recalled the magical words of the engine driver writer whose enthusiastic outpourings under his 'LBSC' pseudonym had enriched the pages of *The Model Engineer* in the 1940s. Finally, after some dual and a briefing, I sat astride the raised track leaning forward to gingerly open the steam regulator and do my first solo on a steam locomotive; rare privilege indeed.

It was time to do something about those 'N' shaped centre section struts. Because each pair sloped forwards and outwards their compound-angle geometry presented the tricky design problem of establishing their true length and the position of the end attachment holes. I did some full-size drawing on the long-established basis that if you can draw it you can make it. The rear strut and the diagonal are joined together at the top end so I made a wooden jig to hold them and got 'Taff' Hatchard to weld them. It seemed that the best way to proceed would be to prop up the centre section in its destined position and drill the top ends of the strut tubes through from the attachment plates on each face of each spar which is what I did. By October, when the local newspaper reporter called, the two fuselages rested snugly side by side. Like aeroplane builders the world over we dreamed of flight. At the end of a long day, a passer by, looking into John Urmston's tiny workshop, might have been startled to see two balding, bespectacled men sitting in plywood boxes, smoking pipes and drinking beer.

That year saw publication of Ernest Gann's classic, *Fate is the Hunter*. Its poignant truth was tragically emphasised on the afternoon of 1 November when Silver City's Senior Captain, George Hogarth, and his first officer were snatched from our midst. No longer should we enjoy his comfortable presence standing at the centre of an animated group in the bar. It was hard to believe he was gone, unflappable, experienced, exuding confidence. For long hours we speculated on what could have happened. The basic facts were simple; his Bristol 170 was making a routine flight from Cherbourg to Guernsey with a payload of three cars and seven passengers. In low cloud, he passed over the Guernsey airfield, radioed he would go round again and in deteriorating weather missed his second approach. The engines were opened up but the aircraft swung to the right and continued to fly slowly until it struck the ground.

A year passed before the appearance of the Accident Investigation Branch report. When the engines were opened up, auto-coarsening of the starboard propeller occurred and the Captain would have had no indication that this was not the result of engine failure. Strip examination of the cut-out switch had disclosed the fitting of a non-standard spring which fouled its casing. It was a grim reminder of the power of life and death and the ever-present responsibilities of the aircraft engineer from whom the utmost integrity must be demanded.

It was becoming increasingly obvious that we needed more working space. The assembly of the Fury wings would have to be tackled next. The main spars had long been carefully stored, supported on wooden blocks above the concrete floor, against a wall of the workshop. I thought long and hard about the problem before reaching the obvious answer. One evening I drove to the Doc's house in my VW Beetle. By fully winding down the front passenger window, I was able to slide my eight wing spars into the car as far as they would go which left a foot or two projecting forward, slightly askew. Under cover of winter darkness and in a freezing draught, I set off discreetly homewards, feeling rather like a jousting knight; if the spar projections should hit, at best a lamp post, at worst an innocent pedestrian, the opposite ends would surely shoot smartly forwards to wallop the back of my head.

In my bedroom I set up two spars on two small wooden trestles, dusted off my wing ribs and, armed with clinometer, trammels and a few small tools, began assembly of my first wing. By Christmas, snow lay on the ground, wood shavings on the bedroom floor and an electric fire struggled to maintain an acceptable gluing temperature.

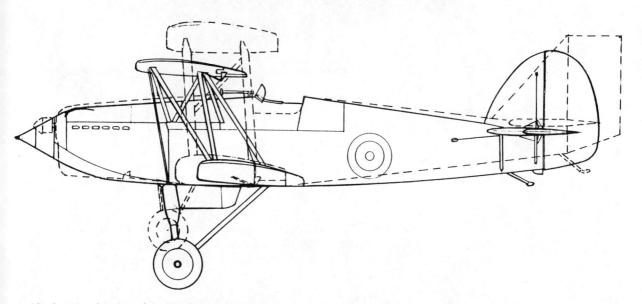

'A side elevation drawing of the Hawker Interceptor super-imposed over that of the Wot . . .''.

John Isaacs in his newly completed Fury I.

CHAPTER 8

FURY FANCY (1962–1963)

Fury wing construction was traditional and straightforward. The wing ribs had been made with two, carefully-jigged, rectangular gaps left in their Warren-girder framing to allow them to be slid over the two solid spruce spars. The latter, supported near each end on two trestles, were levelled until both were horizontal, checked by the machine-gun clinometer; truly rectangular in plan, checked by trammel between pencilled datums on each spar. Correct alignment proven, the two spars were joined by gluing in two compression struts built up of spruce and ply, one at the interplane strut anchorages, the other half-way inboard towards the ply-webbed root rib. None of the ribs was yet fixed, which allowed them to be eased along the spars to give some latitude in fitting wooden diagonals between compression struts; where diagonals crossed, the anti-drag braces were cut to butt on the drag members, the joint being sandwiched between ply biscuits. Since these diagonals were doubled in bays inboard of the interplane struts (i.e. one pair connecting spar top edges and another connecting bottom edges), an unusual degree of rigidity was built into each wing panel. Biplane wings, commonly built with wire bracing in a single plane, tend to be very flexible until held firm by interplane struts and wires on final assembly. With compression struts and diagonals glued in place, it

Fury bottom port wing.

became a simple matter to position and secure ribs to spars. On the top wings an aileron spar was slipped into outboard ribs before fixing the wooden wingtip bow, itself made from glued laminations in the same fashion as the fin leading edge.

Experience with the Club Currie Wots had indicated that one basic wing panel could be assembled in one week of full-time work. In the case of the Fury top wings, the built-in six foot ailerons had to be cut out afterwards and holes for the three hinges carefully marked and drilled.

The large rooms in the big, old house allowed the four wing panels to be stacked against the bedroom wall while I dealt with other matters.

Construction of the Fury had forged ahead of the stressing so, in winter cold and in summer heat, from time to time, we built up a record of the aeroplane's strength. On evenings when we bent over slide rules, calculating, checking, plotting graphs, tabulating figures, I waited with bated breath to learn whether alteration of my completed handiwork was required. Ray Hilborne would mull over a problem, reach for a reference handbook, gaze into space for a minute or two, and pass inconsequential comment while he thought. A burst of frenzied activity followed, slide rule slipping smoothly to and fro, figures quickly jotted down. Sometimes, in the tense, expectant silence, strange pattering sounds on the caravan roof startled me; to my unspoken query Ray answered, 'I wish the birds round here wouldn't wear hob-nailed boots all the time.' More silence was broken by the hiss of indrawn breath and a muttered 'Tutt, tutt' but never a sign from the great man's inscrutable face for he liked to tease me. Suddenly he scribbled a last figure, underlined it heavily, threw down his biro with a flourish and announced, 'Well the load in that member is 1,670 pounds.' Mustering every ounce of insouciance I inquired, 'Is that good?' 'It's OK' said Ray, or, if it wasn't, as my heart sank lower and lower he cheerfully remarked with stressman's guile 'Ah, but we haven't yet considered the 'X' factor'. When he did, to my utter relief, success was usually assured for he had a good brain and I came to feel that no matter how great the disaster he would find a way round it.

Stressmen are a special breed, the whole strength calculation process starts with an assumption of applied loads and it seemed to me that at every step along the way an instinctive sense of self preservation had taught them to build in 'funk factors' which would allow them, under pressure, to begrudgingly give a little so that in moments of dire necessity they seem able to toss in some forgotten factor or conjure up an alleviating circumstance.

The zenith of all our efforts on each part of the aeroplane was to arrive at a reserve factor (RF), always underlined in red to shine like a beacon among the mass of figures, symbols and sketches which adorned each page. Theoretically, good design is symbolised by an RF of one, if it is less there is a weakness, if more, an excess of strength and weight. I tried to adhere to designer Bill Stout's dictum, 'Simplicate and add more lightness'. In idle moments, I pondered on the impossibly perfect design where, with all RF's exactly one, every single part of an overstrained aeroplane might fail at the same moment − what spectacular disintegration!

As the evening wore on, Ray, a shortish man whose amply-covered frame belied his earlier sporting days as a runner, would cast increasingly frequent glances at his watch for he was a disciple of designer Harold Bolas who reputedly claimed that 'All problems are soluble in beer.' Who was I to argue?

And what of the Halcyon twin? After putting in 1,000 hours, I had ceased work on the project when I began a full-time teaching career at the Technical College. Just as I had been pre-occupied with a new job, no less had been the Patron with his turbine Wot development. Nevertheless, there was progress and by the middle of the year, Ray Hilborne had left Handley Page to set up a drawing board in the clubhouse and put in twelve months on design. Whereas the aeroplane had been originally envisaged as a two seater the later firm commitment to four seats turned attention from the 65

The Halcyon G-ARIO in Spring 1962.

hp Walter Mikrons to the larger 100 hp Minors built by that same Czechoslovakian company. The Minor was a splendid little engine roughly equivalent to the de Havilland 'Gipsy Minor' and the Patron arranged to go to Prague to collect two.

Accordingly, he had set off in the Rapide, accompanied by Owen and Grace Hill. Beset by impassable weather they landed in Luxembourg and hired a car to continue the journey. The transaction at Prague was apparently carried out in a motor car for they were not allowed inside the factory. Furthermore, while the Patron dealt with the business, the Hills were almost arrested when, despite then fashionable long skirts, Grace had the temerity to cross her legs as they sat in a workers' tram. The engines were carried out and placed in the car together with their propellers, the whole being listed merely as two engines on the manifest. Back home, away from the bizarre experience of that unhappy country, our own Customs officials insisted on moving the propellers to a store in Southampton as they were not mentioned specifically on the engine documents.

The only exception to the generally wooden construction of the Halcyon lay in the landing flaps which were of aluminium-alloy design and which were made by Vickers apprentices, thanks to S.P. Woodley. For the three undercarriage legs, in the interests of economy, it had been decided to adapt existing Lockheed tailskid oleo units as produced for the Sea Vixen. As these naval jets were catapult-launched in tail-down attitude the oleos could receive very hefty thumps and were consequently designed to be very stiff. The intention had been to give them more springiness by enlarging the damping orifices inside the struts.

When the bulk of the design work was accomplished, Ray left the club before the airframe was completed and so was not present when the sandbag proof-loading tests (for which he had supplied diagrams) were applied. The tailplane, subject of some concern due to the small fuselage cross-section at its anchorage, gave no problems but the wing skins showed signs of unexpected wrinkling; however, there is some evidence that they may have been overloaded. In late spring 1962, during taxi trials over Eastleigh's rough surface, tragically the rear spar failed. The aircraft was put into storage, later to be burnt and by 1964 G-ARIO was removed from the Civil Register. We had all learnt from the unhappy episode.

The Prime Ministerial 'You never had it so good' might well have been directed at Hampshire Aeroplane Club members but it was not to last; 1961 had already seen many changes of fortune. The Airport had not been closed as scheduled but sold instead to a private purchaser; for us life was never again the same. Our Irish instructor had left and was replaced by James Douse. Now, in the summer of 1962, we suddenly learnt that the Patron was going; he had accepted an advertised post for a flying instructor with the United Nations Organisation in Tunisia. He had sold the club to business-men John Habin and Owen Hill.

During his reign of nearly eight years each week had brought a new experience, a new crisis, a new adventure, a new opportunity, a new

'. . . top wings and centre section were laid out on the lawn'.

delight. We had each been privileged to enjoy his generosity, to accept his leadership, to share his knowledge, to benefit from his wisdom. His philosophy was always to help others unstintingly. An airport kid, willing to wash aeroplanes, might get a circuit at the end of the day and enough circuits could lead to a coveted pilot's licence. Some made it and became airline pilots; others squandered opportunity, yet he seldom complained. Tyro engineers were encouraged in the hangar because he appreciated that they might one day retrieve his aeroplane when it fell into the 'bundu'. His open mind was receptive to new, sometimes outrageous ideas and always he was a sympathetic listener.

As the fortunes of any club are variable he claimed it cost him money every time we flew the aeroplanes so, if we were going to 'prang' them, he joked with an eye on insurance, 'Don't forget, deep water or a box of matches.' During one difficult week in the early days, staff wages came from Owen Hill who simply turned up with them for, he said later, 'I didn't like to think of the bods going without their pay.'

At play too, his charm lay in a spontaneity sometimes pointing to adventurous outcome. There was, for instance, the summer evening when half a dozen or so early arrivals at the club learnt of the seventy foot boat he had just acquired. Within minutes the clubhouse was empty, doors were left open and a scribbled note placed on the bar, 'Gone boating, back soon'. We were not back that day, instead, adrift on the Hamble in the monster with a flat battery.

Despite such apparent light-hearted behaviour the fact remains that he had successfully steered the club through seven-and-a-half precarious, eventful years. There had been bad moments – a Rapide emergency landing on a French beach in darkness for example. Again, the club Auster, a notorious 'floater', had overturned when a member was landing; as we watched the incident the Patron calmly said, 'He could have saved the day with a quicker burst of throttle.' A popular lady member suffered similar indignity when a gale-force gust swept the Auster on to its back as she landed at Exeter. A divine providence seemed to protect us and, as Owen said years later, 'He gave us all so much at a time when he had nothing.'

The golden years were gone; Vivian Bellamy had brightened all our lives with a spark of adventure.

I attacked the Fury with renewed vigour. I had made, from a length of angle-iron, a simple universal reference gauge with which to set the root attachment fittings on wings, centre-section and fuselage. To verify alignment, the skeletal 21 foot span top wings and centre-section were laid out, assembled, on the lawn. Also, I proved the aileron control circuit as its operating cables passed round pulleys within the centre-section and thence through the wing to the bellcrank.

From London there arrived a bolt of Irish linen. Its standard width of 54 inches required the joining of two or more lengths side-by-side to span each wing. To make this joint the edges of two lengths are folded back, one downwards one upwards and fitted into each other, just as one might curl the fingers of each hand and interlock them; they were then machine-sewn with a double row of back stitching. The balloon seam or 'French fell' so formed was to lie chordwise. With linen, it is important to first iron out any creases before the material is draped over the structure and the two abutment edges folded under, at the trailing edge, for overhand sewing, eight stitches to the inch, with a lock stitch every two inches. To the therapeutic qualities of such rhythmic activity can be applied the mental stimulus of computing the completion time, based on the achieved sewing speed.

It is advantageous to do fabric work in summer to best meet the temperature requirements for doping, that is, brushing on the strong pear-drop smelling cellulose liquid which, on drying, will seal porosity and shrink linen to the desired drum-taut surface built up by successive coats, so this became my priority task. If done in damp or cold weather, the drying dope will blush which, contrarily, means it will dry out with a lacklustre, patchy white appearance.

As far as I was concerned, the greatest seasonal boon was that I could slap on the costly dope with the bedroom windows open wide for ventilation. I found that if I started in the morning the fumes had diluted sufficiently to allow natural sleep by nightfall. As many coats were necessary, and each must be allowed to dry, the whole process was spread over some days. I thought I had read somewhere that drinking a pint of milk was supposed to be a good antidote to the fumes but, at club evening socials, I found my request never taken seriously.

After the first coat of dope, one inch cotton tapes were stuck over each rib boom and I began 'stringing', using waxed linen braided cord rolled flat on its reel and of great strength; the old RAF hands called it 'kite' cord. Its main purpose is to secure the fabric to the ribs to maintain wing shape and it is threaded through a large needle of at least nine inches in length as it has to be pushed through top and bottom fabric surfaces close alongside the rib, round the rib and back up through the other side to form a loop around the rib. Each loop terminates in a special seine knot from which the continuous cord extends, outside the fabric, along the edge of the rib boom to the next loop, the pitch between each being three inches. Pulling tight each knot is hard on the hands and soon causes a sore index finger. Two-inch wide serrated-edge tape is then doped over all 'stringing' and small vent eyelets are stuck to the underside fabric near the trailing edge.

While waiting for dope to dry, in spare moments, I turned to *The German Giants* reading, spellbound, of the 138 foot span biplanes of 1918 with their 15 foot wing chord. Gratefully, I turned back to 'stringing' my mere 3½ foot ribs with nightmarish thoughts of nearly 60 seine knots needed on one huge rib of the Staaken!

When the wings were covered, Mike Evans kindly delivered them to the 'factory' where I was to paint them silver using the Doc's borrowed compressor and spray-gun before storing them in his loft above the workshop.

Turning to the undercarriage, despite consideration of motorcycle fork-type sliding tube units to simulate the real Fury's long oleo legs, I finally settled for the simple fixed tube Vees with axle tied into their apices by heavy braided rubber cord, universally known as 'bungee'. The method had served us well on the Currie Wots as it had on the aeroplanes of the First World War.

The wheels posed a greater problem. Standard wheels for commercially-built aircraft employed fat, low-pressure tyres intended for, heavier, two-seaters. Scaled representation of the fighter's large narrow tyred wheels demanded something different and I sought help from Dunlop; correspondence lasted from June till October. My unusual requirement specified an outside tyre diameter to suit the scale. The nearest solution lay in the use of standard 3.25 × 14 heavy-duty scooter tyres while my 'original design' hubs were turned by Doug Peacock, on a massive six inch Dean, Smith and Grace lathe. Each unbraked wheel was then assembled, using forty 10 SWG spokes, by a local specialist who built wheels for the motorcycling trials fraternity.

It was time to install the engines. These had lain for many months alongside the steam locomotives in John Urmston's pantry ever since we purchased them from Peter Clifford, the Omnipol agent for Czech aviation industry products. Advertised as new and still in their original crates they were 65 hp Walker Mikron III four-cylinder in-line aircooled engines for each of which we had paid £250. They were exceedingly neat little motors resembling a scaled-down version of the 'inverted' Gipsy Major and they were believed to be no longer in production, regrettably, since there was nothing else comparable.

Constrained by the size of the workshop we found it necessary to pull the fuselages back until their sterns projected through the open window into the yard to make sufficient room at the front end for the engines to be correctly aligned, supported on their packing cases with space to move round them. In these cramped conditions we filed and fitted our steel tubes for the engine bearers which John then tack-welded in place. Frustrated by the absence on holiday of our usual willing welder, 'Taff', we were fortunate when, with the aid of a friend of John's, we managed to get them finish welded and stress-relieved, professionally, at a nearby factory. When the engines had been mounted and the bearers proven the fuselages were dragged forward again into the shop to protect the stern ends from the elements and the window was shut. I pushed the Fury right up against one wall to allow John a measure of freedom for it was obvious that I could do no more serious work until I moved out, though I was able to busy myself with lesser tasks.

On paper, I lofted the engine cowlings. Around the slim in-line Mikron it was not too difficult to devise conically-derived shapes for top and bottom contours which would be easy to make from aluminium sheet although the nose portion with hemispherical chin, propeller shaft hole and offset cooling-air inlet orifice was more demanding. Thus I was able to evade the worst excesses of messy glass-reinforced plastic (GRP) cowling construction in which I was to become embroiled a decade later. Even so, for the one small nose bowl, a rough wooden framework became the basis for a fair weight of plaster of Paris the surface of which, we found, could only be satisfactorily smoothed by use of a Surform as ordinary files clogged hopelessly. On completion, I took it to a local firm who first laid up a female mould in GRP and from that, a male nose cowl.

Educated in the ways of the Aeroplane Club where the junk pile served also as a general store, I acquired potentially useful bits and pieces from old aeroplanes as opportunity offered, although, seen in retrospect, sometimes with a weight penalty. From an Avro Anson, I had retrieved a heavy brass Ki-gas priming pump, aluminium pitot tubing was ripped from plentiful scrap Tiger Moth wings, a Venturi from a fuselage, while wooden interplane struts suitable for cutting down to size were bought for five bob a piece.

It was to finalise the length of the latter and to establish flying and landing wire requirements that I so urgently needed space to temporarily assemble and rig the aeroplane.

The scaled Fury had solid spruce interplane struts. Three were used on each side to form non-adjustable rigid N struts. This denied the alteration of incidence that is possible on a Tiger Moth where a pair of parallel pin-jointed struts are braced by diagonal streamline wires. Varying the lengths of these allows the flexible wing panels to be warped at will.

The rigger's incidence achieved with my (stiffer) wings would depend on the accuracy of the root attachments (already determined) and on correct lengths for each of the three separate struts making up the interplane N. Their calculation was a challenging geometrical problem.

Consider a wing with no dihedral but with its chord set at a marked angle of incidence, viewed from the tip. Assume it to be attached to a fuselage by fore-and-aft fixing bolts lying in the plane of the chord. Now raise the tip to give an appreciable angle of dihedral. As the wing pivots

The Fury in the chicken shed (Clifford Olding).

upwards about the root end, the leading edge at the tip will move upwards at 90 degrees to the bolt axis and therefore rearwards, introducing an element of sweepback.

The Fury's lower wing has more incidence and more dihedral than the upper wing and hence a greater sweepback. Dihedral pivot axes are at different distances from the aircraft centre-line and there are 19 inches of stagger at the root. Furthermore, the struts themselves slope towards the upper wing tip when viewed from the front. With so many variables it would have been imprudent to cut the interplane struts irretrievably to length before rigging the aeroplane and taking measurements to verify calculations. The old adage always applies; measure twice, cut once.

On a dark stormy winter's evening a stranger walked into the bar. He wore a long navy-black mackintosh coat of the type common to airline pilots, with uniform trousers visible beneath. Confounding the unpleasant weather he remarked how glad he was to be back on the ground implying that he had flown from London. He appeared several times in subsequent weeks and let it be known that he would be taking over part of the hangar alongside the club. He was expecting the arrival of two Broussard aeroplanes from France any day. Learning of my space predicament he gave generous assurance that I could tuck my little aeroplane in a corner of his hangar. As the days wore on and no aeroplanes appeared, it became a standing joke to walk out on to the tarmac, peer up at the sky expectantly and say, 'I'm just waiting for the Broussard.' It never came. The last I heard of him was that the club's new manager had driven him to the railway station, where he borrowed ten quid for a ticket, and disappeared for ever.

More welcome was a chance encounter at the bar with a Mr Kemp who said he might be able to help me as he owned some derelict chicken sheds on his father's property a mile or two from Botley. He himself was flying map-making photographic surveys in the sole example built of the Reid and Sigrist Desford twin, its long nose witness to earlier prone-pilot experiments. In time, I was invited to inspect the sheds and to meet his father, a charming elderly gentleman whose name rang a bell with me. James McCudden's *Flying Fury* memoir had been on my bookshelf since I was 14, so I dug it out and, to my joy, read that the great VC had indeed watched Ronald Kemp's remarkably fine flying at Farnborough in 1913. Further it was known that he became an early test pilot of Short seaplanes and, between the wars, a director of the Air Survey Co of London and Rangoon. Delighted to find my host so celebrated a personage, I asked if I could have the use of a shed for three months, to which he agreed, refusing to charge any rent.

There was a snag. The previous occupants of the shed had left ample evidence of their tenancy in the form of knee-deep straw and droppings which might be classed under the generic term of chicken-litter. I had to clear a space. The shed was reached by skirting through Mr Kemp's garden to the far end of a field where it lay at the bottom of a steep slope, flanked by a drainage ditch. When the channel sometimes became obstructed, I often found pools of water collected on the clay floor. Armed with a spade and a borrowed wheelbarrow, I spent several weekends in wellington boots shovelling, digging and dumping the litter outside.

I was not cut out to be a farmer, so when the wooden shed was about half cleared, by the middle of March 1963, I decided to move in. Again Mike Evans supplied transport for the short journey to the village after we had prised the fuselage free of John's workshop and extracted the wings and tail surfaces from his loft. Almost two years after the project started, I felt I was getting somewhere.

In my temporary hangar, I placed the fuselage slightly askew to allow room to walk around it. Undercarriage Vees were bolted back to the forward fuselage and the tailplane to the rear. The centre-section was mounted on its outwardly-splayed rigid N struts and the tail-end of the fuselage lifted on to a trestle and packed until the top longerons were horizontal both longitudinally and transversely. Since the spoked wheels and tyres were not yet available, the rigid undercarriage vees gave firm front support with no worries about tyre deflection upsetting the rigging attitude. As incidence was already established, the art now lay in tensioning the two pairs of cross bracing wires that pulled the centre-section to left or right until it was both symmetrical and normal to the fuselage in plan. To check symmetry, I dropped a plumbline from the rear spar at each side and measured the distance of each from the bottom longeron. To steady the lines against draughts the bob weights were suspended in little jam jars of oil, a dodge picked up from the Supermarine jig erectors.

An Easter interlude brought a foretaste of joys to come when we moved

Waiting for the truck.

John's Wot to Eastleigh and set about its final assembly, a successful first flight followed a week or two later.

His problems were my problems. We had both elected to use preformed non-corrodible steel wire rope for all adjustable interplane bracing. It was more readily available and cheaper than streamline wires which could only be obtained in the UK to special order from Brunton's of Musselburgh in Scotland. Both ends of each wire had to be secured in the form of a loop to attach the cable to a terminal fitting or turnbuckle. One easy method was to form by special tool a rather unsightly ferrule resulting in a 'Talurit' swaged splice, the other, which we chose to employ, was a more pleasing manual splice using a spike. Since the cable diameter of about ⅛ inch, consisted of seven strands each containing 19 tiny wires it was no easy matter to follow the progress of each strand, correctly entwining with its neighbours throughout 4½ rounds of tucks, despite excellent written instruction in such skills from *Civil Aircraft Inspection Procedures* (CAIP). Fully aware of the catastrophic nature of a failure of a lift wire, landing wire or control wire, I made a dozen trial splices before venturing to use one on my aeroplane where I needed a total of 70; fortunately John helped. Being initially uncertain of the final lengths, we had both prepared one end only of overlong wires prior to assembly.

My lower wings were attached to the fuselage, their tips supported on trestles to give 3½ degrees of dihedral, and their incidence was checked. Because the landing wires from the lower wings are attached at their upper ends to rear spar root fittings on the upper wings, the latter had first to be attached to the centre section, their tips suitably propped or suspended from the roof at one degree dihedral. The three strut attachment pin centre distances were measured on each side, compared with the calculated figures and the struts cut to length and completed. With the struts installed, first priority was to complete the second splice on each landing wire, with these in place the wing structure became self supporting so that the lift wires could be added at leisure. On removing all trestling it was possible for the first time to stand back and confirm my belief that there is no greater delight than a tautly-rigged dainty little biplane.

Control surface cables followed. To achieve the most direct run, the wire operating the elevator top horn ran right through the tailplane as on the real Fury. Each aileron cable ran from the lower end of the stick, round a pulley near the bottom longeron, straight to another at the extremity of the centre section rear spar and thence, inside the upper wing, to the bell crank where a large amount of differential had been designed in. My ailerons went up twice as far as they descended but they were plain and not of the original Frise type. However, I was utterly convinced that improved flight-handling characteristics over the Wot would result from their location in the top, rather than the bottom wing.

As I happily ploughed my lonely furrow it soon became apparent that I was not entirely alone and I had to resort to leaving tempting little morsels of rat poison dotted about the floor. Sometimes I was drawn from the shed on a fine evening by the compelling sound of two Gipsy Major 10s in time to see my benefactor from the club bank low overhead, doubtless signalling an imminent homecoming as he, also, lived in the village.

The axle was tied into the two undercarriage Vees by braided rubber shock cord which had to be kept awkwardly taut during the binding. Too tightly wound and a hard landing would bend the axle, too slack and even at rest the axle would ride high out of its tubular fork. A loose-fitting loop of 'check' cable overlay the 'bungee' to safeguard the aeroplane if the rubber gave way. I collected my wheels, slid them and their retaining collars on to the axle stubs, fitted their securing bolts. The aircraft was mobile.

An abundance of work remained. The tinned steel tank had to be installed, an ON/OFF fuel cock devised, instrument panel fitted, cowlings finalised, Ki-gas primer pipes joined, an Urmston 'snifter' valve incorporated, pitot pipes clipped, seat attached, safety harness secured, oil pressure pipe connected, oil temperature gauge fixed, throttle coupled, cockpit door assembled, windscreen constructed. As I sought to anticipate potential requirements, each journey from home added to the inventory of paraphernalia cluttering a temporary makeshift bench which bowed

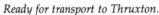

Ready for transport to Thruxton.

beneath boxes of nuts, bolts, washers, woodscrews, rivets, unions, fasteners, 'P' clips, clevis pins, rolls of tape, pieces of ply, spruce and aluminium, assorted springs, string, cable, copper pipe, small tins of paint, brushes, varnish, dope, thinners and oil. And, at the beginning and end of each day, I carried my toolbox between car and shed, a routine which, at other places in other times, endured for many a long year.

Then, by the end of June, I was ready. It was a simple matter to remove all wing bracing and slip off the wings and the seven foot strutted tailplane with elevators. Measurement of the shed doorway had indicated a very tight fit. The critical factors were the 51 inch width wheel track and the height of the centre section; reluctance to remove the latter, so carefully rigged true, finally caused me to let most of the air out of the tyres and we just squeezed under the lintel. The fuselage was manhandled over the ditch, hauled up the slope, pushed across the field, through the garden to Mike Evans' truck parked in the leafy lane. It was so easy, roll the wheels on to the horizontal tailboard which rose like a lift at the touch of a button, push forward again until the nose cowl nudged the back of the driver's cab, wings flat against the fuselage side, tailplane flat on the floor, tailboard hinged up, climb in beside Mike, neurotic anxiety slipping beneath low-arched bridge or overhanging trees but, above all, exaltation.

Thruxton again. It was like coming home. Sqn Ldr James Doran-Webb now also busy with go-kart construction, allocated me a small Nissen-like hut isolated from the big T2 hangar. It was high summer and biplanes abounded as the current crop of ATC cadets circuited the field in the indigenous fleet of Jackaroos. In the little hut the tailplane was reassembled and I busied myself on lesser tasks for a couple of days before soliciting the help of a cadet or two to put the wings on. This was done out in the sunshine as the doorway was not wide enough to accept a full span; accordingly at day's end the Fury was pushed a few hundred yards into the big black hangar among all the biplanes where John Urmston's red Currie Wot was already resident. In a dark corner lay one of the few monoplanes, the abandoned mock-up of the four-seat braced low wing Paragon.

In the long Summer vacation, daily I drove the 26 familiar miles to isolated Thruxton. Out in the country half a mile beyond the Test river bridge, an encroaching majestic tree narrowed the road. By chance the rough painted warning band on its broad trunk gave approaching motorists perfect illusion of a white terrier to add further enchantment to the sinuous by-ways leading to treasured Thruxton. I loved that airfield; I loved its remote wildness. Of its wartime origins, visible remains lay in the crumbling black-tyre-streaked runways, the perimeter track, the black-painted T2 hangar at the foot of a gentle slope half a mile from the watch tower block with its offices, kitchen, canteen, bar and a handful of bedrooms. Alongside, a Nissen hut served as flying control, classroom and shelter for a Link trainer. Presiding over this little empire as general manager was the CFI, John Heaton, whose generous, warm-hearted, extrovert personality bewitched us all. On the flying side he was assisted by shortish Bill Leary

The Bugatti Type 57 at the Medjez el Bab war graves cemetery.

and, part-time, by RAF-moustached local pig farmer, Sqn Ldr Ramsay Smith, and sometimes Colonel Hallmark from Alderney.

The day came to start the Mikron; its logbook showed a bench run of seven hours 25 minutes in April 1957. It started easily but the needle on the engine revolution counter ran backwards. The fuel tank, interposed between the instrument panel and the engine, precluded the use of a direct flexible drive for the tachometer. I had therefore acquired an electrically-driven unit, not liked because it registered double the engine speed and so demanded constant simple mental arithmetic. When we reversed the two electrical wire connections at least normal clockwise needle rotation returned.

Three bathroom scales were placed, one under each wheel, one under the tailskid, the sum of their readings indicated 540 pounds empty weight. Adding the statutory but optimistic 170 pound pilot, 73 pounds for ten gallons of petrol, 17 pounds for oil and oddments, it rose to the 800 pounds AUW which had been the basis for our calculations. By taking moments, the designed centre of gravity position was also confirmed.

Like professional pilots, ground engineers are a nomadic tribe so it was not difficult to get 'Brit' (J.R. Brittain, holder of A, B, C, D and X licences) to vet the aeroplane. He gave me a short list of jobs to do but signed his satisfaction so that documents could be completed and application made to the PFA for a Permit to Fly.

I had already taxied the Fury but now suggested that Col Hallmark might like to see how it felt. His fast run reflected his views when the little machine lifted off to a height of five or six feet. Now convinced it would work, elatedly I took a pre-arranged holiday break while the paperwork was processed.

Spoilt by Hampshire Aeroplane Club expeditions, I had never flown by scheduled airline before I set off from Heathrow with Vivian Bellamy's schoolboy son, Charles, Tunis bound. From Le Bourget we rode Tunis Air's Caravelle flown by an Air France crew; training the Arabian line's own pilots was the raison d'etre of the Patron's UNO job. I noted his taste for regal toys was undiminished as we climbed into his 3.3 Bugatti Type 57 which waited in the hot darkness at El Aouina airport; secreted in his villa garage was a 1,000 cc Vincent HRD.

Moustache and beard now gave him a rugged Ernest Hemingway look somehow suited to the desert. The villa, tended by an Arab girl, M'bruka, was comfortable, but I trod the bathroom warily. A previous visitor, on picking up a flannel, had been badly stung by a scorpion lurking beneath, although its unwelcome presence was said to be very rare.

We had just missed a long spell of oppressive heat but school flying in Comanches and Aztecs still began at 7.00 am and ceased at lunchtime to avoid the worst excesses of summer turbulence. One morning, silent backseat observer on a navigational exercise, I, too, traversed the country peering down, when alerted, at traces of derelict airfields whence, long ago, Me 109's had risen in anger. Afternoons passed pleasantly on beaches, exploring, viewing Roman remains, airfields and the beautifully-kept and tear-jerking war graves at Medjez el Bab and Carthage; once we had a brush with gun-toting police. Evening meals improved with Tibar wine from the local monastery. Returning to England, alone, on a delayed flight, a missed connection at Paris was exploited by completing the last leg in an Olympic Airways Comet flown with spirit.

The Permit to Fly was waiting. At Thruxton, I set about the minor tasks 'Brit' had commanded. Then one afternoon it suddenly struck me that there

John Heaton taxies in after the first flight of the Fury.

John Heaton and Fury at Thruxton at the time of the first flight.

was nothing else to do. I drove up to the tower and asked John Heaton if he felt brave. The little Fury was the first of its breed. Nobody knew for certain how it would behave and I was much out of practice; it is wise to leave it to the 'pros'. But as builder, even more so as designer, a consciousness of the burden of responsibility for the test pilot's well-being will always add a tinge of anxiety to the high pitch of excitement of a first flight.

John walked round the aeroplane making complimentary remarks as I briefed him on the layout. Then he climbed in, took off, flew round for fifteen minutes, made a low run past the spectators and landed. His great guffaws proclaimed his obvious delight. His only criticism was a reported slight tail heaviness. It was a valid comment although I was aware that he himself weighed a full 230 pounds. There is no trim arrangement on the Fury but it would be a simple matter to pack up the front tailplane spar to increase incidence. I stayed at the hangar, carefully inspecting the aeroplane, lovingly patting the cowling and generally fussing over it, reluctant to leave. By the time I did arrive at the clubhouse bar, John had the first bottle of champagne open on the counter in a gesture typical of that great-hearted man. It was a euphoric evening of utter contentment and, for me, a historic day with no hint of what was to follow the construction of that simple little aeroplane in later years.

From the start, I had anticipated possible tailplane angle change by incorporating an adjustable fork end on each of the four external bracing struts. When the hardwood packing blocks were made and the incidence proven, I installed new fixed-length struts of greater rigidity.

In September, out of the blue came a congratulatory letter from the great man himself, Sir Sydney Camm. He had been shown a photograph of my aircraft and wished to call and see it when passing; unhappily he died without it proving possible.

As opportunity offered, under John Heaton's guidance, I got back into flying practice on the Tiger Moth, nearest we could get to a two-seat Fury. He climbed out and stood by the runway, a great, lovable teddy bear figure energetically urging me on again to give encouragement after each practice landing. Then it was my turn.

Not more than a minute or two in time yet a lifetime's memory. I sit in the Fury, dry-mouthed, and push open the throttle, committed. The tail comes up, speed increases, easier to keep straight now, we clear the ground, unexpectedly the starboard wings tilt sharply down, dismay as the woods beyond the hangar start to swing across from the right, they disappear below as I will the aircraft upward, straighten out, more left rudder, village council houses fall away, glance at the ASI – 65 knots, cautiously turn to port, more height, another cautious turn, level off at 800 feet, superb view over or under the eye-level wing, 70 knots on the ASI, rounded wing-tip tracks along the runway, passes it, turn port again, crosswind, gauge the distance, check the altimeter, close the throttle, hear the wind soughing in the wires, sinking, check airspeed, roll into wind, check airspeed, stick back, sinking, feel life leaving once buoyant wings, don't let the wheels touch, I hear Bert Hawkins' disembodied voice, 'Stick right back in your balls,' we touch, keep her straight, don't relax. Phew!

Self-consciously I glanced at the little knot of spectators and decided I hadn't got the tail quite high enough on take-off. (There was to be a sequel). Propelled by the age-old rule, 'always finish on a high' and aware of the guilt of my first take-off, I opened the throttle again. I was learning.

Big, burly, gentlemanly Bill Hardy was a charming man of taste, his presence usually signalled by classic open 'blower' Bentley, dainty, period Austin Seven or equally illustrious motorcycle. For years in fair weather and in foul he had run an excellent flying group operating a Tiger Moth. Late in the year, on a grey overcast Saturday afternoon, I pottered on the Fury in the dark hangar when someone brought word that a Tiger Moth had crashed on the other side of the airfield. Sadly we learned it had been flown by a member of the group who, with his passenger, had been severely injured. On Sunday morning, I volunteered to help dismantle the remains. The Tiger Moth lay on its side amidst the crumpled wings, tailplane pointing to the sky. It had pitched a hundred yards into a field beyond the narrow country road which skirted the aerodrome boundary. A mechanic and I stood in the middle of the tangled wreckage releasing bowed bracing wires and wondering how the occupants had survived when a car approached along the road. Suddenly we heard a squeal of brakes as it slid to a halt, the driver got out, rushed to the wire fence and, cupping his hands, yelled 'Are you all right?'

Isaacs Fury II

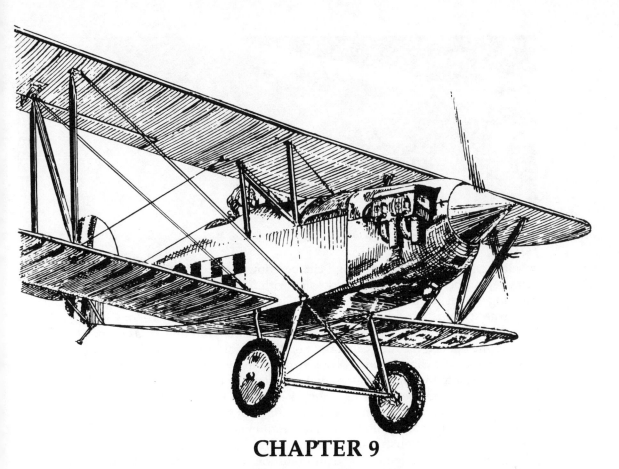

CHAPTER 9

FURY FINALE (1964–1968)

In the North, two DH 83 Fox Moth biplanes had operated for years under the aegis of the Giro Aviation Co Ltd carrying thousands of holiday-makers on joyrides from the sands of Southport. Outside the Aeroplane Club at Eastleigh stood the survivor, G-ACEJ, flown South to renew its airworthiness certificate. In the open cockpit behind the enclosed four-passenger cabin sat its helmeted owner, S.N. 'Gerry' Giroux, rotund in his fur-lined leather jacket. He was already a legend. I had been told that his operation was a sight to behold; he would drive a very ancient motor car along the beach, shouting into a megaphone, 'This is the airport police! Now will you please move back!' When an engine once failed on take-off, his Fox Moth flopped into the sea; extricating himself from the cockpit to swim ashore, he turned and noticed the unharmed passengers standing alongside the aeroplane, knee-deep in water.

As the propeller jerked to a stop he pushed up his goggles, eased the

Gerry Giroux in the cockpit of his DH Fox Moth.

woollen garment from his chin and climbed down to greet 'Brit'. When he removed his helmet, I saw an elderly man with friendly grin, a facial tic and blinking eyelids; behind him the cooling Gipsy began to tick in sympathy. I half expected him to produce a rag and wipe whale oil from his face for Giro Aviation began with World War I de Havilland 6s the year after I was born. Instead, he opened the little cabin door on the port side of the fuselage and two black Scotties came bounding out, barking and yapping. The Fox Moth was pushed into the big hangar ready for its lengthy overhaul.

The club aeroplanes were tightly packed, cheek by cowl, one side of a white line painted on the concrete floor. After some days it was remarked that the Fox lay outside the line and additional hangarage fees were demanded, to the embarrassment of its owner. Fearing that the airport management might attempt to sequestrate the aeroplane, he rendered it immobile by removing a landing wheel and lodging it for safe keeping with Barclay's Bank at Eastleigh.

When airworthiness was reaffirmed and with debts settled, well wrapped against the elements, one man and his dogs rose and headed for northern climes, leaving in his wake the welcome pleasure of brief encounter with a fabled flyer of a byegone age.

At the Hampshire School of Flying, in mid-January 1964, the new director, John Habin, signed a contract to build a replica Avro Triplane IV of 1910 vintage for Twentieth Century-Fox. The design was entrusted to Ray Hilborne because there were no working drawings, only photographic records. A.V. Roe's son, Geoffrey Verdon Roe, supplied historical data and advice on handling was sought from my recent landlord, R.C. Kemp, who had flown the original aeroplane. Placed in charge of the project, which had to be completed by 1 May, was Peter Hillwood, DFC, lately Deputy Chief Test Pilot with English Electric. I was asked to make the wing ribs. An effective little group began work in one of the airport's wooden-framed hangars while, in spare time, I strove to keep up with their demand for ribs from my home. The fact that lateral control was by wing warping instead of ailerons presented Ray with an unusual design task but his simply-

Avro Triplane replica with Peter Hillwood, DFC, and Ronald Kemp, 9 May 1964.

fabricated ribs enabled me to easily meet my quota of about 240. In the event, two flying triplanes were built for 'Those Magnificent Men in Their Flying Machines', together with unassembled parts for a third.

Tall, dark Peter Hillwood lived in the area and he was a dedicated supporter of British Aviation. In the great Battle, he had flown Hurricanes with the RAF's crack 56 Squadron and on 13 August 1940, had been shot down over the Thames Estuary; he swam two miles to the shore and flew again next day. Later, he served as a Spitfire test pilot with Supermarine and more recently he had been test flying Canberras and 1,000 mph Lightning jet fighters.

In February, I was honoured to have a man of such calibre fly the Fury at Thruxton. When he returned from one sortie concerned with static and dynamic stability evaluation tests, he told me in technical terms what he had found. When I asked if such result was favourable, it was gratifying to be told, 'Well, it is better than the Lightning'.

As the Fury was a new type the original Permit had been issued to cover an experimental flying period. For full Permit-to-Fly certification a stipulated flying programme had to be carried out, including the maximum (VNE) dive to 140 mph. Representing the Popular Flying Association F. I. V. (John) Walker joined us at Thruxton. Most talk centred on the controls. Some thought the elevators too sensitive, others considered they should be larger because of a tendency to 'run out of elevator' when the tail came down in landing; there was a discussion on the stick force per G; the rudder was thought to be too light. I stood and listened to the pundits. It was an easy matter to 'heavy up' the rudder by adding a short aluminium angle each side of the trailing edge to create a concave effect. A ground-adjustable aluminium tab was bolted to the port elevator as there were no in-flight trim

'. . . the stack of wings lifted the Triplane easily aloft' (John David Rogers).

Peter Hillwood, 'Brit', and Ray Hilborne with Avro Triplane replica, 9 May 1964.

arrangements. Back at home I made a set of new, wider chord elevator ribs, they were never used.

In March, out of the blue, we received news of the death, after a very brief illness, of the CFI, John Heaton. It was a bitter blow for he was synonymous with Thruxton, flying instructor, guide, counsellor and friend to all. He was buried in the little village churchyard beneath the circuit of the airfield he had known and loved so well for the past twelve years.

At Eastleigh, in May, like aviation's pioneers we rose at dawn to foregather on the airfield before even the slightest zephyr should disturb the early morning stillness as we launched our frail craft. But the Avro Triplane was well-built and its extinct 35 hp Green engine had been superceded by a 90 hp Cirrus of later vintage. Perched high on the triangular fuselage today's pilot, Peter Hillwood, was watched by yesterday's, Ronald Kemp; and by designer Ray and the construction team as 'Brit' swung the propeller into life. Unlike the pioneers, we had no need to lie flat to discern daylight beneath the wheels for the stack of wings lifted the Triplane easily aloft.

Nowadays, driving North, as I swung off the high-road, over the river bridge, towards Mottisfont village, I swear the little white terrier on the tree trunk wagged his tail. At Thruxton, I was becoming accustomed to living with a Fury. Its slight tendency to swing to the right on take-off was easily controlled, it flew itself off in about 100 yards at 50 mph and climbed at 750 fpm. In the air the view was excellent, because of the eye-level position of the upper wing one could look over or under it – a splendid situation during let-downs and steep turns. Those upper wing ailerons with their marked differential were a delight. The stall was below 45 mph with no tendency to drop a wing. For me, the most evocative moment always came when I eased back the throttle and heard above the idling Mikron that

Flying the Fury for the 'Aeromodeller'.

singular biplane sound of the wind in the wires. As the nose came up for the landing flare, speed fell off very quickly and demanded an alert left hand to apply a trickle of power if needed. There were moments of excitement.

At one period the normally smooth running Mikron engine became lumpy and erratic at anything other than full power. As I circled the airfield, every attempt to adjust the throttle setting to cruising revs brought on irregular running. Concerned, I landed hastily and was even more startled to learn that I had been trailing a plume of black smoke. Eventually the trouble was traced to a minute leak in the carburettor float, through which petrol had seeped until the heavy float never rose enough to cut off the fuel supply to the carburettor; thus very rich running ensued unless the throttle was kept open wide. It proved necessary to drill a small hole in the float to pour out the petrol before sealing it again with solder.

One afternoon while practising landings in a busy circuit, I mistakenly landed too close behind another aircraft and stupidly ground-looped off the grass on to the hard runway while taking avoiding action. A few broken trailing edge ribs on a lower wing were easily repaired but for some weeks, I seemed to have unaccustomed difficulty in keeping straight on the ground until, by chance, I found the steel tailskid tube was bowed sideways.

The day Ron Moulton came along to take air-to-air pictures from a

Jackaroo for the *Aeromodeller* in very windy conditions, I made a shockingly heavy landing which, combined with too tightly tied bungee, caused a bent axle. But these were minor problems.

In December, by arrangement, Britain's most successful aerobatic pilot, Neil Williams, paid two visits to Thruxton. As he was then a serving Royal Air Force officer based at Farnborough, by way of a professional exercise, he generously undertook to write a full assessment of the aeroplane. Some of his findings were as follows.

The aircraft was statically and dynamically stable in pitch. Static stability was lower in the stick-fixed case than stick-free, a combination that made the aircraft very pleasant to handle in pitch.

Lateral stability was positive but very low, owing to the lack of sweep and dihedral (1° on the top wing). The differential aileron response was very good and the rate of roll at 90 mph was about 100 degrees per second. The damping in roll was low, owing probably to the low aspect ratio, and this combination gave crisp, precise control in the rolling plane.

Directional stability was good at constant power, and turns could be made with a reasonable degree of accuracy using the stick alone. Pilot-induced sideslips confirmed that lateral stability was very low compared with directional stability. Release of the controls was followed by an oscillation which damped out after three cycles, during which the angle of bank increased and a turn began with the nose falling. This showed normal spiral instability.

The first spins were undertaken and took about 2.5 seconds per turn with the nose 60 degrees below the horizon. The standard recovery technique of full opposite rudder and stick progressively forward stopped

The Fury cockpit (Aeromodeller).

the spin invariably after a further quarter turn. Loops, stall turns, slow rolls and rolls off the top were all successfully accomplished.

In his summary Neil said: 'It has to be flown properly to be really enjoyed, but can be handled by any competently-trained pilot. The excellent harmonisation will show modern pilots just what they have been missing. The ailerons are probably the best I have ever met on a biplane, giving rise to a strong tendency to indulge in four and eight-point rolls. It is a tightly-rigged little aeroplane and feels good in all attitudes. As a serious aerobatic aircraft it requires at least double the power.'

On this latter point discussions with Neil had clearly shown that design of a serious aerobatic aeroplane was a very specialised affair which would need to incorporate such features as symmetrical aerofoil wings: it was a formula which held no great interest for me, but the idea of increased power was valid as various pilots had commented on the need to claw back lost height after each aerobatic manoeuvre which prevented a smoothly continuous display. As the idea grew I kept an eye open for a suitable second-hand engine for new ones were far too costly. To move ahead of my story, after some months of search I was put on the scent of an 0-290 Lycoming engine of 125 hp which seemed eminently suitable to meet the rule-of-thumb power/weight ratio of 10 lb per bhp or better. The eventual outcome was the purchase of this partially-dismantled and incomplete engine, which lay 100 miles away, for a very fair £100.

At the beginning of 1965, the Fury moved to a new base at John Fairey's magical, 700 yard, private airstrip near Stockbridge: it was nearer home, more economical, offered greater security and yet was only ten minutes flying time from Thruxton.

In the early part of that year too, I was laid up and activities slowed down by hospitalisation for, what the doctors called, minor surgery: to me no surgery is minor. Either way the point was that I was unable to take part in the initial building stages of the latest Hampshire School of Flying commitment to build a replica German Pfalz DIII biplane for the film, 'The Blue Max'. The Pfalz had always been a favourite of mine and its slim shark-like fuselage was advanced for 1917. It had to be built in quick time and again, Ray Hilborne undertook the design. Strangely, two of the type were to be made, each by a completely independent organisation and hence of different construction. At White Waltham that master builder, Doug Bianchi, elected to base his on modified Tiger Moth components to save time, whereas Ray chose the more purist route of starting from scratch with ply-covered wooden frames and longerons.

Construction started in April in a small workshop tucked away in the residential Bishopstoke area of Eastleigh and it was at this new location that I was destined to spend some busy hours. When personal mobility returned, I joined the sewing and stitching circle engaged in fabric covering the thin flexible wings. Major components were then transported for assembly at the airport in a hangar which had earlier yielded the Triplane. When the summer vacation began, painting was in progress and it became

Peter Hillwood flying the Fury in the summer of 1964 (John David Rogers).

'The inverted Gipsy Major in the Pfalz. Note 50 lb of lead behind the spinner.

my lot to paint on the black iron crosses. As the original German company had been formed at Speyer on the river Rhein it was amusing to refer to our team as Pfalz-Flugzeug-werke, Southampton am Itchen. With Mike Evans, I spent two or three days rigging the aeroplane. Weight and balance checks were carried out, always hustled along by the panic of meeting the completion target date. A harassed Ray asked me to quickly design a mounting to attach fifty pounds of lead to the front of the Gipsy Major engine bearers. Returned from his desert penance, Vivian Bellamy walked in and by the beginning of August he lightly lifted off the Pfalz, airborne in a matter of yards. Peter Hillwood, who was to carry out such spectacular flying in the film, appeared a few days later to add his assessment. Young Peter Benest, brave soul, arrived to ferry it across the Irish Sea to Dublin and suddenly, rather sadly, it was all over.

Meanwhile, we had collected my Lycoming and stored it in the Pfalz

The Pfalz built for the film 'The Blue Max'.

workshop at Bishopstoke while replacements were sought for missing or unserviceable parts. Now, unhurriedly, I could turn spare time attention to the internal obscurities of the engine, advised by that doyen of licensed aircraft engineers, J. R. Brittain. On the Lycoming the aluminium-alloy heads are screwed and shrunk on to steel barrels so when dye penetrants revealed a cracked head, a complete new unit had to be found and valves ground in. Some new piston rings were called for, hydraulic valve tappets had to be investigated, mysteries of the Marvel-Schebler carburettor resolved. Slowly, carefully, the rebuild proceeded.

Halfway through construction of the Fury I had joined the American-based Experimental Aircraft Association, mainly for the benefits of its excellent monthly magazine, *Sport Aviation*, devoted to the support of homebuilders. One of the first copies I received featured an amphibious monoplane built by a member named Volmer Jensen. Possibly with his Walrus days in mind, the Patron decided to build one. He obtained plans and spruce from the USA, mahogany ply from Fairey Marine at Hamble, and December brought me to his home near Southampton to assemble hull frames on the same table-tennis table which had seen the birth of the Wot. Being flat-sided, they were no problem though this time we used chocolate-brown resorcinal glue. When the frames were complete it was proposed to get an ex-boat builder to put the hull together in the garage. The main keel consisted of a hefty spruce beam which could only be pulled into a curve at the bow by first steaming it into pliancy. After combing the garden for suitable equipment Vivian spotted the very thing. Impetuously he seized on a drain pipe leading down from the roof guttering of the house. It was wrenched off the wall, the keel inserted, and then conveniently propped above an open fire while steam from boiling water passed through. The hull was quickly built but it was to be many years before the aircraft was finally flown, in Cornwall!

Vivian had not been idle since his return from the desert. At Blackbushe he had installed in an Auster V the 118 bhp Rover TP90 gas turbine which that Company had developed from the TP60 used in the Wot. He had flown it first on 13 June 1965 and development continued.

At home, I studied changes that would be necessary to the Fury to install the Lycoming. It was reckoned to weigh about 260 lb against the Mikron's 140 lb so an early decision was taken to re-stress the complete aeroplane for an increased AUW of 1,000 lb. Slide-rule pushing sessions began again with Ray. To accommodate the wider flat-four engine it was desirable to build a wider fireproof bulkhead. Reshaped nose lines around the more powerful engine allowed the bottom cowling contour to fall away, realistically, behind a large spinner in place of the characteristic (though not unattractive) 'chin' of inverted in-line engines.

The advantage of increased power was convincingly brought home to me by an experience on one of my 'off' days. The aeroplane was pulled out of the hangar and routinely inspected. Omission of the latter could be disastrous: I read of an all-time classic case where a pilot attempted a take-

Paul Pobenezny, President of the EAA, with the turbo-prop Auster, April 1966.

off having failed to notice that his partner had earlier removed the rudder and taken it home for repair.

On the day in question I did notice that the muddied ground was very wet and made mental note not to get the tail too high and risk a broken propeller. Consequently, I cautiously opened the throttle and as the Fury lifted prematurely it began gently rocking from side to side. Thoroughly alarmed, I was certain something was wrong with the aeroplane, perhaps with the controls, and I felt that this time I was going to hurt myself. Trees loomed ahead as I drifted marginally to starboard over the ploughed land bordering the strip. I made instant decision that I would try and put down. Seizing the split second when the wings momentarily levelled between their pendulum-like swings, I closed the throttle. The wheels dropped firmly onto the furrowed surface beside the verdant runway and the aircraft stopped, almost at once. Nothing seemed to be broken. Unnerved, I put it back in the hangar and drove to Thruxton. Here, a pilot friend told how, passenger in a Tiger Moth flown by an RAF jet pilot, he had once been similarly carried the full length of a runway before they crashed in the overshoot area.

The Fury had been on the wrong side of the drag curve where, due to the high angle of attack needed to maintain low-speed flight, insufficient engine power was available to overcome the increased drag and it was semi-stalled.

1966 was a year of variety. In April we were visited by the founder and President of the EAA, the legendary Paul Poberezny, and treasurer Art Kilps. Paul's unsuspected talents as a ventriloquist, disclosed by a barking dog imitation, startled lunchtime diners at Hamble's 'Bugle' before we moved on to the airstrip where he flew Wot, Fury and turbo-prop Auster.

The Fury I pictured at Thruxton.

The Fury became the 90th homebuilt aeroplane flown by this remarkable American. Afterwards he wrote, 'I immediately recognised the fine handling qualities and felt at home . . . it is very manoeuvrable and one of the nicest biplanes I have flown.' Two days later he lectured at the RAeS in London and, at the following dinner, formally approved formation of the first EAA British Chapter, to be led by Harold Best-Devereux: Vivian and I were founder members.

In May, in my small garden shed I made the five master ribs for each wing panel for an Avro 504 which Vivian Bellamy had contracted to build for a film company within three months. The following month brought a curious incident with the Fury subsequent to loss of compression on two cylinders of the Mikron III. On removing the barrels and examining the pistons we came to the conclusion that the engine had been assembled with Mikron II piston rings which are three millimeters smaller in diameter; these were replaced.

After a year's development flying, the Rover turbo-prop powered Auster was pretty well tamed so in July I happily seized the opportunity to accompany Vivian Bellamy to Baginton to attend what proved a crucial annual general meeting of the PFA. As we took off from the Stockbridge airstrip, I quickly realsed I was in the hot seat for, to counteract torque, the exhaust gases giving 15 pounds residual thrust were ejected sideways to starboard immediately ahead of the passenger. A propeller pitch control now regulated the cropped Cessna Skymaster blades fitted to the Beech McCauley constant-speed hub. The unnatural smoothness conferred on

Auster flight was demonstrated by balancing a flat-sided threepenny piece on the fuel gauge. After two hours trouble-free turbine flying we scraped back to the strip as the weather clamped.

August saw two first flights. At Blackbushe on the 17th the fraternity gathered to watch dynamic little Maurice Robinson complete the last pre-flight tasks on the Avro 504 which he had, incredibly, put together in 12 weeks. Finally, in the calm of a summer's evening Vivian Bellamy lifted his thumb from the blip switch to give the Le Rhone rotary its head and the recreated, legendary trainer took to the air. Nine days later at Portsmouth Airport it was the turn of a modern trainer. Rovers and Hants and Sussex Aviation had laboured to convert a Chipmunk to turbine status. Again I watched Vivian fly the aeroplane successfully, followed by Ted Hawes. But initial test flights were disappointing and revealed an abysmal rate of climb. Development continued.

By way of contrast, in September I made my last flight in the Fury with the Mikron engine. It had been retained in airworthy condition on the private airstrip while I put together the Lycoming and conceived a plan of action. Thus, in retrospect, the Mikron Fury now became the Mk I as, progressively during the year, the aeroplane was redrawn in its Mk II form.

The first move was an engine switch. In the hangar the Mikron was removed from the airframe and ferried to the plumber's workshop at Bishopstoke from whence the Lycoming was brought to the strip. Since a casual correspondence with an American EAAer had resulted in a firm offer for the Mikron, I was then faced with the irritating diversionary export task of securely crating the engine, dealing with the Board of Trade and visiting shipping agents.

With Autumn came tragedy.

I once flew with Peter Hillwood in his Proctor. In his English Electric days he regularly navigated it between Warton in the North and his Hampshire home in the South in fair weather and in foul: always he got through. Those days were over. Gone were the 14 perilous years of

First-flight day for the turbo-prop Chipmunk, Portsmouth, 26 August 1966.

Avro 504 at Blackbushe on 17 August 1966, with Adam Fisher leaning on a wing.

experimental flying in high performance military jets. Piloting light aeroplanes was, by comparison, 'a piece of cake' for this most experienced and competent survivor of 'the Few', so it was with a sense of disbelief that we learnt of the disaster. He had been hurrying back from Germany to England, where the prototype Islander was urgently required for sales demonstrations, when the aircraft broke up in bad weather over Holland killing him and his German passenger.

It was known that in early stages of testing, this aeroplane had been fitted with more powerful and heavier engines and that the strength of the then unmodified wing did not fully comply with British Civil Airworthiness Requirements; for this reason a number of operational restrictions had been imposed. Two years after the crash the Dutch Civil Aviation accident report presumed that '. . . the aircraft was flown beyond the operating limitations stipulated in its certificate of airworthiness.'

Yet, 15 years earlier, on the eve of the first direct Atlantic crossing by a jet-propelled aircraft without refuelling, unpublicised, Peter Hillwood had been the hero of the hour. The Canberra, flown by an RAF crew, suffered a bird strike on the positioning flight to Aldergrove. Here, while grounded on 20 February 1951 for overnight repairs, it was discovered that a new generator cable was needed from the factory. Without hesitation, Peter Hillwood and his navigator, D. A. Watson, set off in a snow storm into a cloud-base of 400 feet over Belfast; tops were reaching 11,000 feet. The Consul forced through to Warton. Severe icing on the descent resulted in a sliver from a propeller penetrating the fuselage. With the spare aboard, the iced aircraft returned in the frozen darkness to Aldergrove to allow RAF and English Electric personnel to complete their task in the bitterly cold hangar. As *Flight* commented, 'These splended performances were to pass almost unnoticed in the flurry of publicity rightly occasioned by the Canberra's flight.'

In the short daylight hours of winter I made my weekend country pilgrimage to John Fairey's lonely airstrip atop its tree-lined ridge. The hangar lay at its westward end and the normal hazards of its rough, unsurfaced floor of Hampshire chalk were accentuated in wet weather when it became very slippery. There were no facilities: no water, no electricity, no light, no heat.

I set to work on the engineless Fury. The alterations entailed cutting out the existing engine bulkhead and chiselling away the forward longerons and diagonal cross braces from the 1½ mm ply sides, easing out brass brads as the work proceeded. The ply sides were then pulled out parallel and a new, wider bulkhead glued in, together with new forward top and bottom longerons and diagonal bracing. All drilling, of course, had to be done by handbrace.

A study of potential weather conditions became a matter of interest because of the Aerolite gluing requirements. It would have been useless to glue parts, even during a reasonably mild day, if a cold or frosty night was likely to follow to prevent proper curing.

Working alone, the need for some form of engine slinging device became of paramount importance so that the 260 odd pounds of Lycoming could be handled. I sketched out a simple gantry, rather like a child's swing, and checked sizes for clearance on a Fury drawing. Ian Musson, who ran a general engineering workshop in Southampton, offered the use of his power saw and workshop to cut up steel angle to make the gantry. I deliberately designed it to be dismantled into 3½ foot lengths which would fit across the back seats of a Volkswagen. For slinging I used a Haltrac hoist, an admirable little self-locking unit employing nylon cord of 1,000 pounds breaking strain, which weighed only 1½ pounds and cost little more than £10. The gantry worked well and with the Lycoming now hoisted roughly in position it was possible to verify clearances and practicalities of the engine bearers.

At home, more angle iron was cut to make a simple rigid jig in which to place the tubes ready for welding the engine bearers. When the bearers were complete it proved possible to install the Lycoming in the airframe single-handed. Sometimes in the depressing depths of winter, typically, Vivian Bellamy would arrive to stand and watch and lend more encouragement

Pastoral scene at Kings Somborne airstrip in 1966 with (left to right) Turbine Chipmunk, Currie Wot, Avro 504, Isaacs Fury.

until, unable to stand the chill any longer, we would drive to the village pub for a lunchtime hot pie.

In December the blow fell. At Southampton airport for 15 years scarcely a week had passed when I did not visit that humble wooden clubhouse where, after Vivian Bellamy's departure, Owen Hill and John Habin had struggled to keep open the Aeroplane Club for another four years. Now, given notice to quit by the airfield owners, they were forced to close their doors. The Hampshire Aeroplane Club, one of the best in Britain, had been founded over 40 years before, had trained hundreds of pilots, many to serve the nation well in time of war. It was a bitter blow; no longer would we enjoy the Friday soirées. Down from the ceiling came the big four-bladed wooden propeller, down from the bar came the 'first solo' beer mugs, away went club competition cups and trophies – all for storage. Even the road sign within the airport entrance 'disappeared' after the well-attended final supper party on Friday, 30 December 1966. It was the end of an era and I stayed late, insistent on being last to leave, for I knew we had all lost something rather precious. I never went back.

The new year ushered in fresh divertissement. For years the inner recesses of the mind had retained memory of a book review I had once read. The book was in French and told the epic story of Aéropostale, forerunner of Air France. Now, with the aid of French friends from the Hornet Moth 'incident', I obtained a copy of Jean-Gérard Fleury's *La Ligne*. It was heady stuff; so armed with French dictionary and hazy recollections of schoolboy lessons I busied myself translating this 110,000 word Odyssey into English for the wonderful tale has never been done full justice in our language and St Exupéry's irresistible writings had filled me with insatiable desire for more.

Meanwhile, as I plied my lonely weekend trade in the hangar alongside the airstrip, on occasion a Landrover would nose its way into the field driven by the farm manager, Reg Butler. A shortish, lean and delightful countryman, who had spent his whole life in the vicinity, he would offer a cup of tea from his flask and friendly chat. He told me how, on a Summer evening, the estate owner, Sir Richard Fairey, would stand with him on the ridge surveying the peaceful village below, the undulating downs, the Test river valley, the wooded slopes, the timeless glory of England until, raising a hand in gesture at the wondrous scene Sir Richard would say, 'Faireyland.'

The great pioneers who founded the British Aircraft Industry had chosen well for on the slopes across the valley Sir Thomas Sopwith had settled.

After a long hard winter's work we started the Lycoming which ran smoothly and sweetly. I borrowed bathroom scales to record an empty weight of 704 pounds for the Fury and a satisfactory centre of gravity position. Although shorter than the Mikron, and located slightly further aft because there was no separate oil tank to accommodate, the heavier Lycoming did cause a forward C of G shift in the laden aeroplane of some

The Fury II in the markings of No 43 Squadron, RAF.

four inches. Consequently there had been fears that the landing wheels might have to be brought forward to combat the resulting tail lightness. Although my aeroplane had no brakes it was believed that the Hawker Furies had been prone to nose-over with too fierce a brake application on landing. When we put it to the test such fears were unfounded.

In May, Vivian Bellamy took a mere 50 yards to lift the Fury easily from the 700 yard strip in 'dirty', uncowled condition. It was still a docile aeroplane without vices and very pleasant to fly. With the power almost doubled, the rate of climb soared to an exhilarating 1,600 fpm and the test pilot was soon indulging in loops, rolls and stall turns with happy abandon as it was no longer necessary to pause between each manoeuvre while the underpowered aeroplane clawed back lost height.

Although I had drawn the proposed nose lines, cowlings did present a problem. Current practice was to form a plaster mould actually on the installed engine and lay-up glass reinforced plastic (GRP) on this. However, with the aeroplane stuck in a field 16 miles from home, this was not a pleasing prospect and anyway, for a Fury, nothing can replace the appearance of burnished aluminium. Forming sheet metal to give two-way curves (so easily obtained in GRP) is a highly-skilled and dying art in which I had not been trained. Eventually, at a modest engineering firm in Southampton my plea fell on receptive ears when the manager, an old General Aircraft sheet metal man, agreed to put some apprentices on the job. I lofted the contours full size, cut out an armful of hardboard templates and deposited them on his doorstep. I believe he had done most of the work himself when, a few weeks later, I collected the various pieces of double-

The Royal Air Force roundels were painted on at Netheravon.

curved aluminium and rushed them over to Taffy for welding into cowling panels.

Now, anxious to avoid a nose-heavy aeroplane, I spent a month or so fiddling with a lightweight aluminium cowling support framework before, in mid Summer, I decided it was not going to work. While I thought about it I completed my French translation, found someone to type it, drew original sketches to illustrate that noble story and approached publishers.

It will be recalled that initially the performance of the turbine powered Chipmunk was disappointing and, as it had been finished later than intended, Ben Gunn had to use all his test pilot's cunning to convincingly demonstrate the, apparently underpowered, aeroplane at Farnborough in 1966. Only later was the problem identified and solved. Air was originally taken in around the base of the spinner, through a mesh and into the cowling before being drawn into the side intakes of the engine, resulting in an unacceptable power loss. When external elephant-ears were cut into each side cowl to give a more direct intake the climb performance was transformed. Thus with some 100 hours flying on it and surge virtually eliminated by the introduction of a valve and the propeller setting 'tuned', it was inevitable that the now relatively docile aeroplane should appear at the airstrip.

When flying an aeroplane in company with an amateur with any pretension to being a pilot, Vivian Bellamy, would, at some stage, and no matter how unfamiliar the type, unexpectedly hand over control to the tyro. It might happen in the last 50 feet of an approach with a carefree, 'O.K. you land it,' resulting in a flurry of activity, hands reaching for controls, feet groping for rudder pedals to meet the challenge; or it might happen when already lined up for take-off, signalled by a nonchalant wave of the hand towards the throttle and a simple, 'O.K. off you go.' Thus was one converted instantly from the role of interested passenger to the more demanding status of pilot-in-command with its attendant rigours and responsibilities. Then, the precept became listen and obey since salvation lay in carefully following all instructions from the voice of experience. So, I could hardly claim total surprise when, in August after two brief forays, I found myself alone in the Chipmunk flying the familiar circuit, perhaps doubtful of the finer technical complexities of the turbine but clinging, as a survivor to a lifebelt, to pure cockpit rote. It was a smoothly-exhilarating experience. When the aeroplane next flew, the following morning, the maestro had to make a hasty landing when red warning lights gave indication of minor internal turbine trouble.

In the Autumn the cowling problem was picked up again. Starting afresh, a detachable welded steel tube framework was evolved. Concurrently I had been put in touch with someone who was able to produce the spinner. This was an essential feature of the whole cowling concept and, the diameter at the aft edge being no less than 15 inches, it was formed from flat aluminium sheet on a spinning lathe. A carburettor heat box also had to be designed and made; although the uncowled flying had

The Fury II in flight near Basingstoke.

been done without one, we were always conscious of the omission. By mid May 1968, with the cowlings finalised, the empty weight of the Fury had reached 720 lbs which, allowing for pilot and fuel, was within our stressing figure of 1,000 lb AUW.

Fortuitously Vivian was recently returned from Spain where he had been flying for the film, 'The Battle of Britain', in the course of which he had personally flown every type of aeroplane used, including the camera-bearing Mitchell. In such capable hands was the definitive Fury II tested. A top speed of 115 mph was recorded and the raised VNE of 160 mph was reached. As the elevator ground-adjusted trim tab was found best left in a neutral setting, it was removed.

In order to attain a close resemblance to its progenitor, the new nose lines had been simulated, as near as possible, by ignoring the two cylinder heads which projected from each side into the cooling airflow as in the Piper Cub. The overall impression of the Mk II version was now much more akin to the Hawker Fury and to complete the illusion it seemed justifiable to paint the aeroplane in the colourful pageantry of pre-war RAF markings. A letter of enquiry to a government department had disclosed, after several months delay, that the use of National markings could not be legally prohibited but the practice was discouraged and in any event, under no circumstances could I use RAF serial numbers. A courtesy letter to the Association Secretary of the currently disbanded No. 43 Squadron, the Fighting Cocks, for permission to use their famous black and white chequers brought happier, positive response.

There were no facilities for spray painting at the airstrip. With an offer of help from engineer, J. R. Brittain, and the connivance of an enthusiastic Army Major friend, the Fury was flown over to Netheravon where, fittingly, in a hangar on one of the oldest Service airfields in the country, and with the due humility of a civilian, I painted on the proud roundels of the Royal Air Force. Here, too, some further flying was undertaken including, by chance visit one day, a stimulating impromptu display by Supermarine's Dave Morgan, long famed as the pilot who had delighted Farnborough crowds with a masterly performance in an early Swift in conditions which had kept the specialist 'all weather' fighters firmly on the ground.

Then, quite suddenly, the Fury days were over; or so it seemed when G-ASCM was sold and flown off to a new home at Biggin Hill: but there was to be a sequel.

Whereas construction of the HAeC Currie Wots had brought me dozens of letters from other enthusiasts, this was as nothing to the massive volume of correspondence generated by the Fury which now brought fame if not fortune. From all over the world, year after year, hundreds of letters had to be answered; all seeking advice, information, constructional drawings, assurance, encouragement, even jobs in my, non-existent, company. Coming, as they did, from the humblest fledgling to the most senior pilot, from the totally inexperienced to the most able craftsman, they proved an education in themselves. The love of little aeroplanes and the joy of flight knows no boundaries and the impact of such international friendships upon my own affairs will be told later.

Meanwhile, it was amusing to reflect that the little Fury had started with a set of *Aeromodeller* plans and, when I had drawn my three-view GA, the Isaacs Fury was added to their catalogue in its turn. Amongst others, local modeller Jack Morton built an excellent ¼ scale flying model of my 7/10 scale Hawker Fury which performed splendidly in the National Championship competitions.

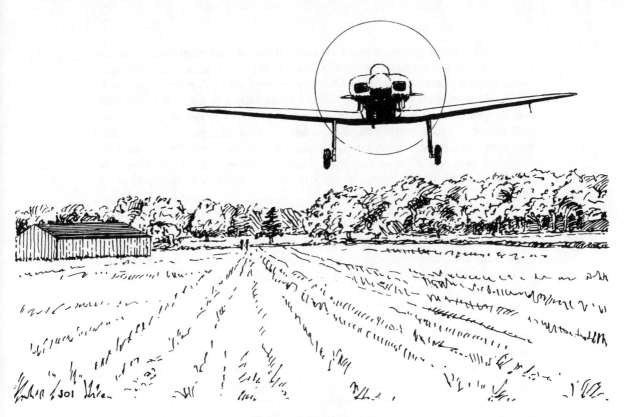

CHAPTER 10

SPELL OF THE SPITFIRE (1969–1975)

After my Fury had first flown, it was suggested that I should build a small Spitfire. Reproduction in miniature of the alluring curves of that dainty monoplane presented a formidable challenge compared to the simple box-like structure of braced biplanes but the seeds of an idea were sown and I began to think about it. Studies continued intermittently over several years. Since I was conditioned by the Fury design philosophy, my intention was to produce a similar-sized aeroplane capable of flying on an economical 90–100 hp engine.

The basic problem with all scale replicas is that the pilot cannot be scaled down. From this fact two difficulties follow. Firstly, if a scale is chosen such that the cockpit is large enough to accommodate a man, the aeroplane may be bigger and more costly than desired. Secondly, simple calculations on the principle of moments may determine that there is little hope of achieving a suitable centre of gravity position.

By using the original Spitfire co-ordinates to accurately draw the external geometric shape of the aeroplane, it became an engrossing exercise to conjure up varied scale general arrangement (GA) drawings within the self-imposed parameters. Only after carefully plotting GA drawings to ¾, 7⁄10, 5⁄8 and 9⁄10 scale, and giving detailed consideration to each, was the latter finally selected in 1968. That it took several years to arrive at this decision may be attributed in part to vacillation between the glamorous fighter and a two-seat high wing monoplane; I favoured a cross between the admired Tailwind and an economical little Piper Vagabond seen at Thruxton. Romanticism won the day as, more and more, I fell under the spell of the Spitfire.

As in all aeroplane design there had to be a compromise; the art lay in one's ability to camouflage it. On the drawing board, at 9⁄10 scale the 22 feet 1½ inch wing span compared nicely with the 21 feet of the Fury and a thrifty 90–100 hp four cylinder engine would balance the pilot if the cockpit was pulled slightly forward and judiciously enlarged to accept the flat, jointed-limbed manikin which I made.

For the magnificent wing and the elliptical tail there could be no compromise; they must reflect the original exactly. A subtle swelling of the fuselage was necessary. Because of the 'fixed' height of the pilot's head, any attempt to blend the fuselage contour into scale vertical tail surfaces gave a downswept humpy Hurricane-like appearance. For this reason I retained a true straight top profile and planned a discreetly larger-than-scale rear view canopy in place of the simple sliding hood of early models. For directional stability, and to offset rudder blanketing effects at the 12 degree ground angle, the large side areas of a Mk XIV fin and rudder were chosen. The fundamental nose lines of the Mk IX allied to the deeper 'chin' contour of the Mk XI PRU version promised well to encase a Continental 0–200 engine. By such subterfuge was the external shape settled; internally a fresh start was required to produce a simpler, wooden structure.

All aeroplanes start as a dream. Somewhere in the designer's mind there has to be a vision of something beautiful sitting out there on the airfield in an indeterminate future. Absolute certainty as to the correctness of concept is essential before total committal. Intensive study, a kind of mental soakage in its atmosphere, induces a 'feel' for an aeroplane and, as if to give substance to the shadow, it is helpful to make comparison with past reality. To confirm choice of size, on to my Spitfire draughtsmanship I overlaid a drawing of the sleek Chilton monoplane; it strengthened my gut feeling.

Ray Hilborne assented to my request for stressing help, his task now eased by one of the new electronic desk calculators: at first I checked its arithmetic by slide-rule. Filled with optimism, we explored basic technicalities lest there be unseen pitfalls which might dash high hopes even before we began the spasmodic evening disciplines which were to lead to 200 foolscap pages of calculations and 24 graphs.

Varying the wing area as the square of the scale size, the original 242 square feet reduced to a mere 87 square feet. Uncertain as to the validity of a

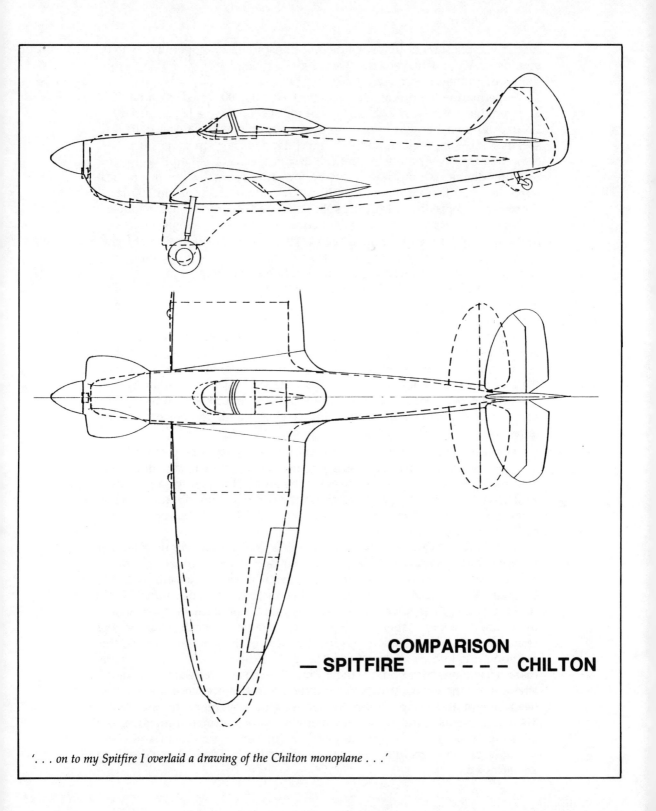

COMPARISON
— **SPITFIRE** – – – – **CHILTON**

'. . . on to my Spitfire I overlaid a drawing of the Chilton monoplane . . .'

cube law application at first we aimed, it transpired, too hopefully, at 1,000 pounds AUW. If achieved, this would give a wing loading of 11½ lb/sq ft compared to the subject aircraft's 26 lb/sq ft.

Supermarine Technical Office Report No. 30,000 dated 30 June 1938 declared that the NACA 2200 series aerofoil section gave a lift coefficient of 1.4 flaps up and 1.84 flaps down so it was a simple matter to calculate stall speeds of 56½ mph clean and 49½ mph flapped. For stressing purposes, computations gave (purely theoretical) design speeds of 158 mph cruise and 284 mph diving. We did no serious performance estimates but in practical terms believed the aeroplane should reach around 150 mph on 100 hp. I chose not to reproduce the small split flaps, particularly as their geometry and operation was complicated by dihedral and a forward swept hinge axis. In the light of Fury experience it seemed reasonable to suppose that flying characteristics would mirror the known excellence of its progenitor; only later would the full significance of this become apparent.

Much has been made of the allegedly too-narrow track of the Spitfire's outward retracting undercarriage although none of the pilots I spoke to admitted this had been a major problem. I consulted *Landing Gear Design* by Conway. Theoretically it is the relation of a narrow track to the CG of the aeroplane which is important. A line drawn from the CG to another, connecting main and tailwheel contact points, forms an included angle with the ground which should not in any circumstance exceed 60°: on the Spitfire this angle is 60°. I decided to widen my track to improve ground stability and lessen any danger of overturning sideways and, to consider inward retraction.

For ease of handling I wanted to build the wing in three pieces but the old bogey of getting adequate bearing in timber caused me to abandon metal joint plates with their forest of heavy bolts and I plumped for a one piece wing from tip to tip. We had to establish the wing load distribution to allow detail design of the 22 foot main spar to proceed. The task was complicated by the geometry of the wing.

A 1948 copy of AP970 *Design Requirements for Aeroplanes for the Royal Air Force and Royal Navy* became the basis of our calculations. Appendix 3 dated 1 April 1947 Clause 3.5 was headed 'General Case of Curved, Tapered, Twisted Wing.' That the merits of this method would confer higher structural integrity followed when we read that 'Prior to the development of the Prandtl theory, tapered wings were commonly dealt with on the assumption that each section was independent of those on either side, this method being known as the ''Strip Theory.'' It can be shown that in many cases calculations based on this theory may lead to an over-estimation of the strength of the wing structure, and hence the more accurate method described in this chapter should be used in preference to the ''Strip Theory.'' ' Thus, guided by the methods of a German Professor, we calculated and plotted wing load distribution, bending moment and shear force diagrams for the full semi-span to enable the box spars to be designed and stressed.

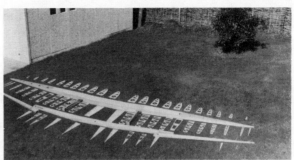

'. . . a modest start on the tail surfaces . . .' (tailplane).

Wing components ready for assembly.

The more I schemed, the more difficult it became to find space for retracted wheels within the slim fuselage or slender wing. Oh, if only it had been a thick chunky-winged Hurricane, how much easier life would have been! An early decision was needed, so after prolonged mental struggle, regretfully, almost guiltily, I settled for a simple fixed undercarriage. Years later, as if in vindication, an authoritative *Sport Aviation* article by the inimitable Tony Bingelis stated, 'No matter how you look at it, constructing and installing a retractable landing gear is a long, expensive ego trip and one should ponder it a lifetime before embarking on it.'

For maximum efficiency the two box spars utilized the full depth of the wing and so split the ribs into three portions each of which had to be carefully butted on to them. The scaled elliptical-plan-form wing has two degrees incidence extending 18.6 inches from the aircraft centre-line thereafter having a linear twist along each semi-span, terminating in a small negative angle (washout) at the extreme tip. The six degrees of dihedral also starts at the twist origin. To accurately draw the front spar shape, all 23 original rib stations were plotted although only alternate ribs were needed, each being different in contour, chord and thickness. The aerofoil's 12¾% thickness chord ratio at the spar root fell dramatically to about 8% at the zero incidence station near the tip and, proportionately, the spar depth and width reduced from 7½ inches and 4 inches respectively to little more than 1¾ inches and ¾ inches. Such slenderness compelled me to skin the entire wing surface with 1½ mm birch ply to achieve torsional stiffness.

Meanwhile, at the Technical College, I had long been cast from the old Workhouse and banished to the outer darkness of an annexe lodged in an old Seamen's Mission, built about 1880, half a mile distant and near the docks. Within its confines a high-roofed chapel had been split into two by the erection of a hardboard partition which formed the back wall of my classroom; behind it budding dental technicians grappled with the intricacies of their trade. On my side, in brief moments of respite, I could gaze, over 24 heads bent over drawing boards, at two small chalk marks on the wall. No-one else knew they were spaced exactly 22 feet 1½ inches apart and symbolized the limits of my vision of the future, the boundaries of my dream, the span of my Spitfire.

By Easter 1969, I reckoned to know where I was going and a small amount of spruce left over from the Fury was sliced up to enable me to make a modest start on the tail surfaces while I continued to think about the wing main spar. Frankly, this worried me as it was to be a 22 foot long built-up, curve-tapered box and I was short on experience of this kind of thing. The spar was the backbone of the project and if that could be built the aeroplane could be built. I considered having it built professionally but the cost was unattractive.

Then came the breakthrough. The Popular Flying Association, in their wisdom, considered me suitably qualified to voluntarily act as an inspector of other people's aeroplanes and I was asked by a man wishing to build a Turbulent to act in that capacity. As he lived nearby we also agreed to jointly order materials. Together, we visited Camper and Nicholson's South-ampton Shipyard. On hands and knees, we peered at the ends of timber baulks to verify that the growth rate was at least six rings per inch before gambling on what their dirt-darkened exteriors might conceal. It is said that the hour will produce the man and in Leslie Broomfield I had found the man.

Early in June, the sheer bulk of two massive beams each eight inches by six inches in section, one 24 feet in length, astonished the principal of the wood machine shop where I had planned to have them cut. Realising they were an embarrassment, I at once offered to get them removed but he said, 'Well, I did promise.' In a few days they were reduced to manageable proportions. I had decided to laminate the spar booms from 5/16 inch thick planks and a more than adequate quantity was so cut while intelligent guesses were made as to what other sizes might be needed. Leslie's more modest requirements centred around a Taylor monoplane to which design he had now transferred his allegiance.

If that spar worried me it did not appear to daunt Leslie whose considerable talents had become apparent. Like the doctor before, he had shown me a superb model steam locomotive and further evidence of his prolific endeavour lay all about – oak panelled walls, parquet floor, dining-room table, chairs, grandfather clocks, glass-panelled front door – all were crafted with his own hands. A bulging workshop housed Myford lathe, bench drill, pistol drills, electric sander, plentiful planes, clusters of G clamps, sash cramps, a veritable arsenal of chisels, a selection of saws, jar after jar of screws, nuts, bolts, tin after tin of unseen treasures. And he was a fully-qualified cabinet maker of the highest order; this was the man who had asked me to vet his workmanship on a simple little aeroplane.

A one-piece spar and associated jigging takes up a lot of space and we cunningly contrived to build it on the floor of the carpentry classroom in a local school during the Summer vacation. The jig was made by screwing six inches by one inch wooden floor boards to cross battens to form a 24 feet × 2 feet flat base. On the virgin timber I drew out the spar shape in pencil, the six degree dihedral line originating either side of the three foot wide straight centre portion. At 18 inch intervals we screwed wooden blocks outside the spar contour and to these in turn we screwed a redwood plank, on edge, set flush with the drawn, curved contour. First, each spar boom had to be assembled separately. The top (compression) boom consists of seven pieces progressively shortened so that at the tips only the outer one remains.

As in all jobs, the secret of success lay in preparation. As a precaution against the spar sticking to the jig, thin polythene sheet was interposed. Each of the seven long boards had to be individually supported for the application of glue or acid on alternate sides. A system is essential, one man handling the glue spatula, the other slopping on acid; under no circumstances must the two come together until all parts are coated since the glue is 'away' at the merest sniff of acid.

The next half hour proved a traumatic experience. As we slapped the glue over the four inch wide boards the copious two pounds of powder I had premixed dwindled rapidly and we began to spread it more thinly while the sweat dripped off us. It must have been one of the hottest afternoons on record and I was truly thankful to have specially ordered GPM slow-setting hardener. From the moment we brought the seven coated boards together, which started the 'curing' process, speed was vital. The wet planks slipped and slithered freely and the torque of tightening clamps sent them skating way from the marked positions. Suddenly Leslie let out an agonised shriek, 'Quick undo them, the polythene is nipped between two boards.' Furiously, I began unscrewing clamps until another frenzied yell of, 'OK, carry on' reversed the process again. Somehow, we got everything reasonably in place within the next 20 minutes; there was nothing else we could do as the glue was setting fast in the oppressive heat. Somewhere beneath that assortment of 48 large G clamps and sashcramps lay the top boom. Emotionally exhausted, I helped clean up the classroom.

In a day or two the top boom was removed and the wooden blocks and redwood plank repositioned on the jig to allow lamination of the four boards which comprise the bottom (tension) boom. Some work was then necessary to clean up and cut the 22 foot long booms nearer to finished shape. Taking advantage of our temporary surroundings they were, on occasion, clamped in the vices of two or three woodwork benches at the same time to avoid a whippy overhang while they were worked on. Steps caused by the progressively shorter laminates had to be planed away to produce a smoothly-tapered inside surface thus avoiding undesirable stress concentrations due to sudden change of section. Surplus timber was removed to approximate the spar width taper in plan; the front face of each boom had to be planed truly flat ready to receive the full span forward ply web.

The last jigging stage was to remove the redwood plank, rearrange the wooden blocks to locate both booms in their correct relative positions, forward face uppermost, while spruce blocks were cut, fitted and glued between them at rib, undercarriage and wing attachment stations. Finally, the forward 3/16 inch ply shear web was glued on to join the booms, scarfed joints being necessary to make up the full span.

It was an exciting moment − lifting the strong stiff spar from the jig just three weeks after we had begun screwing floor boards to battens. It was incomplete and much careful detailed shaping remained before the aft web could be secured but, thanks to Leslie's generous help, I now knew the project was viable. With the end of the school holidays threatening, we hastily dismantled the jig, evacuated the premises and placed the embryonic spar for temporary storage in Leslie's double length garage.

Before the Summer was out, the perennial problem of keeping in practice to retain a pilot's licence was solved in commendable style by the generosity of another friend. Not for me the neoteric nosewheel novelties; contentedly, I ambled over the Plain, surveying the scene from the wind-protecting cabin of a well-bred biplane, each landing on the historic, lush, green sward dictated by the tail-down skills of former times. From the fragile security of the Jackaroo's cabin, high over the airfield I watched the bodies come tumbling down from a Rapide, for Netheravon was the home of the Army Sport Parachute Club. It was an eerie experience, too, to watch a drop from the Rapide.

We took off from Elstree. Close behind the pilot, I crouched on the one seat in the cabin which was jam-packed with bodies squatting on the floor, each parachute-humped figure with crash helmet and stout boots; they were the Red Devils army display team. For 20 minutes we circled over summer haze. The leader clambered forward over the human pile to reach the pilot and find out, 'What the hell is going on?' Aware of my vulnerable seat I tried to maintain a firm grip on the aircraft structure. Then suddenly there was a heart-stopping bang, a whiff of smoke swirled in the cabin as someone precipitately ignited the smoke canister strapped to his ankle and they were gone, the doorless opening of the empty cabin sole witness to their disappearance.

The passenger seats in a Rapide are flimsy, unstable affairs; they have three legs from which projecting tongues slide under metal straps on the floor; the seat is fixed by a single 'pip' pin. They are therefore easily and quickly removed. We set off to collect a parachute display team. The portside door at the rear of the cabin had already been removed and alongside the aperture the sergeant-major despatcher stood, unconcerned, braced with feet apart and his back to the rear bulkhead. Occupying the only two, forward, seats, the pilot's wife and I were chatting when the engines were opened up for take-off. As we accelerated, her seat came free and, abruptly, she toppled over backwards to slide helplessly down the steeply-sloping floor towards the door opening where the despatcher caught her just as we broke ground.

Parachute dropping can provide excitement too for the pilot. At Thruxton, Peter Pearce's Jackaroo was jerked into a vertically-downward attitude for terrifying moments above the club house when his jumper's parachute prematurely streamed over the tailplane before falling clear. Again, descending rapidly after a drop, a Cessna pilot barely retained control when the cabin floor carpet was sucked through the open doorway to wrap itself around the tailplane.

Starting an Avro 504. Vivian hazards the toothpick watched by son Roderick (J.O.I. is in the cockpit) (Stuart McKay).

More safely, on the ground at Blackbushe, I was enticed into the front cockpit of Vivian Bellamy's Avro 504 and initiated into the mysteries of rotary engine control while he, removing his mandatory blazer, stepped back to do battle with the enormous propeller and fire up the Le Rhone while endeavouring to side step the threatening menace of its toothpick guardian skid. The sequence began by my bicycle pumping the pressurised fuel tank to four psi which allowed fuel to spray into the induction pipe as the needle valve was opened; air had to be adjusted with another lever. Once started, a limited measure of speed control was possible by juggling with the levers but it was the celebrated blip switch which, when held in, caused the engine to almost stop until, releasing one's thumb at the critical moment, the nine cylinders fired again; as the revs rose they had to be cut again. Proficiency only came when the knack had been mastered and after my little game of 'Biggles' I came away personally convinced that many of the wartime training crashes were surely caused by problems of engine handling.

Focusing attention on the Spitfire again, I made the three parts for each of the simple truss-type wing ribs, carefully pencilling on the chord and the front spar horizontal datum lines, the angle between them being the (varying) incidence. The rear spar was also built in three pieces so that the forward-cranked outer portions could be joined on at the wing assembly stage. Between times, sporadic work continued on the main spar until, with the aft ply web glued in place and the horizontal datum pencilled on both faces, we were able to through-drill wing-to-fuselage connection and undercarriage leg attachment holes. Now I could check design weight estimates with reality; the spar weighed a little over 50 pounds. At last the spectre of spar construction was finally laid to rest.

'Biggles' blipping in the Avro 504, November 1969 (Stuart McKay).

That autumn I anxiously awaited planning permission from the Civic Centre to extend a small disused coal shed behind my house into a 24 foot by 10½ foot workshop built of breeze blocks. My application (duly granted) had carefully avoided any mention of the word aeroplane since, with no conception of what is entailed, the uninitiated sometimes imagine that aeroplane builders will be constantly running high-powered aero engines in a residential road.

In December, I had the 'hangar' built and the following Spring the main spar was brought to the new workshop. Here, utilising the old spar assembly jig planks, a 22 foot long table was erected supported on wooden trestles. Above it the spar was mounted in flying attitude with the rear spar centre portion set in correct relative position to allow the spars to be conjoined by two steel tube ties which transfer some undercarriage load from front to rear spar.

I devised a simple method of assembly, which did away with the need to accurately level the long table top, and used the main spar itself as a jig. By speedily packing level a wooden straight edge placed across the narrow table at each rib station in turn, it was an easy matter, by measurement, to arrange for the pencil line on the rib to be parallel with the straight edge: ribs thus fitted automatically produced the linear twist along each semi-span. I was fortunate enough to have Leslie scarf in the forward-kinked outer sections to the centre-section rear spar – a tricky operation since their accurate positioning combined correct dihedral with an upward tilt caused by the 'washout'.

When the nose ribs were in place a spruce leading edge (LE) member was pulled round and glued to each to serve as a buttstrap for top and bottom ply skins; a second, smaller strip was glued to its forward face and the changing LE radius carefully shaped and checked by card templates cut

The Spitfire wing structure.

for each rib. The completed wing structure was inverted on to suitable raised supports built above the centre of the jig table so that the, now drooping, tips were just clear. The 1½ mm ply bottom skins were next glued on over the whole, fairly flat, surface. The secret of overcoming the apparent two-way curvature of the top LE skins lay in fixing the ply panels in short sections over about three rib bays at a time. In this manner the formidable task of building the curved wing proved relatively easy.

As the parts went together I began to feel that stir of excitement again. To me, the birth of a wooden aeroplane is always a thrilling sight as the pleasingly-curved girder ribs, each carefully-fashioned to the dictates of a master plan, take up their allotted positions to form a delicate tracery of biscuit-coloured virgin spruce and ply, combining strength with lightness, to carry man on his greatest achievement — to fly like the birds. The satisfaction of creative artistic endeavour surpasses all else and that it was happening here at my home in Southampton, a mere mile or two from the very factory where R. J. Mitchell's magnum opus took shape 35 years earlier, seemed to lend a sense of history to the task.

Before completing the skinning, I was able to install and prove the aileron control run, which used the lightest and simplest method of stranded cable with only a short final rod linking bell crank to control surface. To prove the full circuit, I temporarily fitted the control column, its bearings and the articulating rod between the spars; they could only be finally assembled after the wing was joined to the fuselage.

The ailerons themselves were of the Frise type with inset hinges so that upward movement of the aileron caused its leading edge to project below the wing contour and thus increase drag on the downgoing wing; conversely a downgoing aileron caused no projection on the top contour. Additionally, I incorporated differential movement and fitted mass balance

'I joined Peter Tanner's Wessex Flying Group' (Chipmunk G-AOUP).

weights as a precaution against flutter. Further, I increased the span inboard to larger than scale size in an attempt to improve what I had always understood to be the least pleasant of the Spitfire's controls.

In August 1970, I joined Peter Tanner's Wessex Flying Group and began an affair with Chipmunk G-AOUP which was to last well into my retirement.

Next, turning my attention to the fuselage, I first lofted its shape to a reduced scale on the drawing board and, working from the scaled down real Spitfire cross-sections, I widened them slightly in the cockpit area gradually reducing the increase so that they tapered to almost exactly 6/10 scale again at nose and stern. From this layout I worked up a full size nest of fuselage frame outlines. A print was pinned to a board of about three feet by 2½ feet and covered with polythene sheet. By locating the various members with removable blocks each frame was assembled in turn. The slightly-curved fuselage sides were cut from spruce boards while the rounded tops and bottoms had to be pre-laminated from thin spruce strips before all parts were assembled with ply gussets and spruce corner blocks.

My assembly problem was how to ensure that the wing would match the fuselage correctly; with a workshop only 10 feet wide it was clearly impractical to build the whole fuselage 'in situ' on to the wing, yet somehow I had to build my quart-sized Spitfire in my pint-sized 'hangar'. I knew that the fabulous Falco wing was integral with the forward fuselage which then had a 'transport' joint aft of the wing but I did not want to go to such complicated jigging lengths. After some thought I decided to start by making the forward part of the fuselage on the wing, to ensure fitment, leaving short lengths of longeron protruding aft to which extensions could

The forward fuselage with short lengths of longeron protruding aft, March 1971.

Fuselage in jig, wing stored.

be scarfed later. Thus the four wing attachment holes were drilled in the relevant frames which were bolted to the wing spars while I built the forward sructure around them from the firewall back to the cockpit. When the completed rigid framework was disconnected from the wing the latter could be stored, nose down, close against the shed wall.

Meanwhile, in April 1971, the correctness of my 6/10 scale decision had been happily confirmed when the remarkable EAA President, Paul Poberezny, on a visit to England, walked into my humble 'hangar', enthused over the wing and said in his quiet shrewd way, 'It's the right size.'

Since the top longerons provide a natural horizontal datum, it was preferable to build the fuselage upside down. To secure its straightness over the whole length, some of the original spar jig floorboards were used to build a platform round its outside contour at top longeron level. A string drawn tightly from nose to tail served as a centre-line while, at marked frame stations, wooden crossmembers bridged the platforms ready for the inverted frames to be clamped, athwartships alignment being achieved by matching frame and jig centre lines.

The simple jig was made in a day and the pre-assembled forward fuselage placed into it, upside down, to allow the aft portion of the (inverted) top longerons to be scarfed on. The rear frames were aligned in the jig and fixed to the top longerons; only then were the aft bottom longerons scarfed on to the forward stubs to be finally pulled down into the notches in the frames. After carefully fairing top and bottom longerons with frames, I joined them by applying the 2 mm side skin panels and the rigid fuselage could be removed from the jig; the curved top and bottom ply decking could follow later. I rigged up a dummy wing rear spar to which I could bolt the cockpit lever to prove the elevator control cable run; cable routing from the pendent rudder pedals was also checked.

All the load-bearing structural elements of the aeroplane were now in being, albeit not complete. Periodically I sat with Ray, verifying that our strength reserve factors were at least 1.0. Sometimes, by night, as we grappled with algebraic simultaneous equations in pursuit of a dozen or so

Paul Poberezny, EAA president, enthused over the Spitfire wing. J.O.I. at right (EAA).

unknowns it amused me to reflect that by day I had tried to instil in apprentices a facility to solve for two unknowns or, maybe, even three.

That winter, an aluminium fuel tank of 10 Imperial gallons capacity was designed, formed and welded. Ahead of the cockpit the fuselage top decking was made detachable to provide easy access to rudder pedals, brakes, tank installation and the back of the instrument panel. The penalty was that a diagonal strut had to be fitted across the open fuselage top to accommodate engine torque loads. Consequently the tank has a tube running through it to allow clear passage of a smaller, structural tube. On the real Spitfire, the problem of stabilizing the 'open box' was met by using two tubes forming a plan Vee but, being a larger aeroplane, there were two tanks, one above and one below the bracing.

By way of diversion we covered the dusty, concrete workshop floor with wooden floorboards the first of which were provided by the final laying to rest of the original spar jig planks; in today's terms they had proved cost effective.

Despite my careful jigging attempts to match the main components with symmetry, I had to remove that nagging doubt by arranging for the 'heavy gang' to carry all the parts into the back garden one evening for a trial assembly. So for a brief hour the fuselage was squeezed between two garden walls while the wing lay with one tip nuzzling an apple tree, the other nestling in the raspberry canes; the diagonal symmetry between wing tips and stern post was correct within ⅛ inch. Elated, I drove west for a holiday. After maintaining a presence for several years at Blackbushe, Vivian Bellamy was now established as CO of Lands End Aerodrome in Cornwall which thus became the distant destination of many long pilgrimages.

Two uncertain areas of the aircraft now had to be faced; one was the undercarriage, the other the canopy.

I had studied *Landing Gear Design* by H. G. Conway and concluded that rubbers in compression would be the best compromise; they worked well in the Chipmunk. A local rubber manufacturer gave me a handful of samples of varying hardness but no technical data so, with Ray Hilborne, I spent an interesting morning carrying out compression loading tests on a machine at the University during the vacation. From our findings we drew graphs and selected the most suitable sample while my good friend, Tony Clark, internationally renowned in sport pistol shooting circles, machined a mould and I ordered the rubber pucks. With some difficulty I found a supplier of steel tube for the cantilever legs and got Tony to machine phosphor bronze bushes for the telescopic leg. Elsewhere, torque links were machined for fitment (after further reference to Conway) to the front of the leg. I purchased a pair of 5.00 by 5 Dunlop wheels, brakes and tyres as used on the Beagle Pup. It was a relief to be able to slide the legs into their wing-mounted sockets and check for symmetry and forward rake as the relationship of the wheel ground contact points to the centre of gravity was of considerable importance and not easy to alter if incorrect.

'. . . the fuselage was squeezed between two garden walls . . .'.

The fuselage taking shape.

The canopy problem was twofold. First, how should I design it? Should it hinge sideways – probably the easiest solution – or should it slide back as on the original and, secondly, how should I make it? Whether right or wrong, Vivian's advice is always forceful so when he said, 'Go for broke and make it slide,' I abandoned hopes of adapting a sailplane canopy and lofted the purpose-built shape I required, checking it by sitting in the cockpit with wooden battens and card templates over my head. A narrow fighter canopy of 12 or 14 inches base width makes cockpit entry virtually impossible, so I attached the canopy to part of the fuselage decking above the top longeron allowing both parts to slide aft and expose a realistic entry width of 18 inches.

I planned to 'drape mould' an oven-warmed perspex sheet over a teardrop wooden contour. 'Use Jelutong, it's easy to carve' said Leslie. I had a block sawn into two inches by one inch thick lengths, drew different full-size level-line section shapes on each, cut them, glued the laminates with Evo-Stick rather than glass-hard-setting Aerolite and built up a hollow mould. Shaping and frequent checking by template proved easy enough though it took nearly three weeks work to finalize two moulds, one for the fixed windscreen, one for the canopy. I also made the steel tube sliding frame and had it welded.

The difficulties of finding a large enough oven to heat the perspex, the risk of spoiling expensive sheets and the requirement of optical perfection led me to seek professional help and the canopy was eventually drape-moulded in the London area after a local firm had taken six weeks to decide that they were unable to do the job.

The timely condemnation of a Jodel through glue deterioration had released a half-lifed, American built, 100 hp Continental 0–200 engine and its metal, ground-adjustable, Ratier propeller both of which I bought from the two local PFA members who had acquired them. As it would not be immediately required, we struggled up the long staircase to store the engine on the bedroom floor alongside the nearly complete tail surfaces and ailerons. Indeed, I ruefully reflected, four years into the project and not one single component was entirely complete.

No matter how carefully applied, thin ply always seems to form hollows between its fixation areas so that ribs or frames cause a starved horse appearance which I was determined to avoid. I had long admired the incredibly smooth surface finish seen on sailplanes and I went to see champion sailplane pilot and craftsman, Ralph Jones, who advised a German chemical mix of Laromin and Epicote into which light, phenolic micro-balloons could be stirred.

This pasty mess was spread into all unwanted depressions to be smoothed by drawing a bridging steel straight edge across two adjacent formers. After curing, the high spots of the brown mixture were removed with sandpaper block to reveal where a further build-up might be necessary. When almost the whole wetted surface of the aeroplane had been thus filled and sanded, thin madapollam cloth was struck over the ply with clear low-tautening dope and I began to rub. As successive layers of dope accumulated and were rubbed down with 'wet and dry' abrasive paper for days on end, my finger tips actually bled.

To take advantage of the summer weather I decided to paint and Dudley Morgan generously trailered over his compressor on loan for a week. I had intended a Royal Air Force PRU finish but settled initially for plain cellulose silver all over, since it was quickly available and would eliminate the need for the usual protective aluminium undercoat against light rays. Then it was time for a break.

'12.04 Spot Arabs moving along western edge of 21/03 towards ORP – circle them – then into strafing runs. . .' I glanced up and saw no sign of marauding figures with flying burnous, I heard no crackle of rifle fire nor smelt the stifling heat of noontide desert. I saw only grass tufted with yellow-speckled gorse and brown treeless country beyond; I heard only David's charming Cornish drawl addressing me as squire; I smelt hot engine oil but in the cockpit there were no Vickers gun butts only the faded legend taped inside the coaming, memento of a long-forgotten airshow.

Briefly, I was reunited with my little Fury and its new owners at Lands End had allowed me to fly it. To date its career had been adventuresome. While Biggin Hill based, it had been flown to RAF Wildenrath in West

The Fury and Beaver en-route to Wildenrath, West Germany.

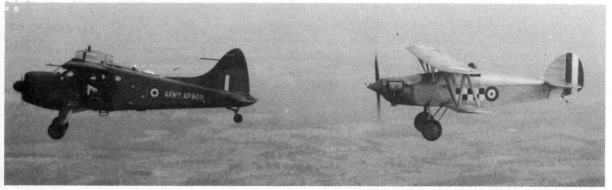

Author in the Fury at Lands End.

Spitfire forward fuselage, engine bulkhead on left (A. J. Clark).

Germany, escorted by a radio-equipped Beaver, to participate in a NATO airshow but suffered the indignity of overturning in the rough on arrival though the following year it had been more proudly displayed before Her Majesty the Queen at RAF Cranwell's Golden Jubilee.

By Autumn, the Spitfire's engine bearers had been made and welded using the modified, steel angle jig built for the Fury. The engine was temporarily installed in the fuselage, then returned with its bearers to the house. The well-rounded cowlings had to be made of GRP laid up on a plaster mould. Some people wrap up the engine and lay plaster over it 'in situ' which results in a condensation-wet, corroded motor which I wished to avoid so I evolved my own method. A wooden template replica of the firewall shape was made and bolted to the engine bearers with engine attached, propeller flange uppermost so that I had, effectively, the nose of the aircraft in the house. Using my lofted nose lines I built a wooden framework around this to ensure clearances but in such a way that it could be 'split', removed and reattached to the dummy firewall bulkhead without the engine inside. In this manner, the engine stayed in the dry house while the wooden framing, supported on trestles in the workshop, became the basis of the 'plug' on to which I fastened wire mesh to retain the plaster.

I bought 112 pounds of plaster of Paris and applied it; it was not enough. Then, for some reason unconnected with my activities, a national shortage of plaster occurred. I scoured the chemists' shops and bought another 56 pounds; it was not enough so I borrowed more from a dental technician. For days and days I rubbed, mostly with a Surform file, until I had a smooth, white representation of the aeroplane's nose.

Suddenly in January 1974, the Arab oil crisis hit the world and, in addition to worries as to the availability of petrol to fly, the price of oil-based plastics began to skyrocket. However, the further advent of some short-time working did help me to enlist the expertise of Ron Rollison who also assisted with materials. The intention was to use 2 oz and 1½ oz fibre glass mat to form smooth-interior-faced female moulds from the plaster 'plug'. From these the desired smooth-exterior cowlings could be formed.

When we laid up the first mould Ron slowed down the setting catalyst and, to my concern, the resin dripped and dripped on to the workshop floor for hours after he had gone home. By mid-February, the female moulds were complete and, its job done, the plug was smashed up and the messy débris of wood, wire, plaster and powder removed to a rubbish tip. A month later the male cowlings had been made and the engine reinstalled on the fuselage so they could be cut in. This time, unlike the Fury, the cowlings were self-supporting, cantilevered from a sturdy firewall bulkhead.

While we were GRP orientated, Ron suggested making the intricately-curved windscreen and canopy external framing of fibre glass which resolved another problem since I had envisaged aluminium but did not know how to form it. The last GRP task, completed later, was to make the spinner, the plaster plug being generated by working a shaped board or template round a centre point just as a strickle is used during loam moulding in an iron foundry.

By May, 1974, in my optimistic innocence, I thought I had a 50:50 chance of completion that summer.

But a thousand interminable details remained and no longer need I use parts salvaged from aged wartime aeroplanes. From the USA came a pair of lightweight Cleveland master cylinders for the wheel brakes; An American fuel filter weighed 7 ounces against the 19 ounce Tiger Moth type; a 2½ ounce Kohler primer replaced the ex-Anson 11 ounce Ki-gas monster (as the engine had an accelerator pump it was not needed); American AN unions and adaptors superceded the old AGS parts for fuel and hydraulic systems. Engineer Dave Ring helped me sort out some connector details while I built up VW mileage seeking parts.

By chance, timely articles in EAA's *Sport Aviation* magazine gave guidance: I read Tony Bingelis on hydraulic brakes, Bingelis on engine cowlings, Bingelis on pressure baffles, Bingelis on exhaust stubs.

In mid-August disaster struck. As I enlarged a drilled attachment hole in the hard-won canopy to accept a rubber grommet, the perspex cracked and a piece broke out of the forward edge. When I recovered from the shock, I found that cutting off one inch from the front removed the damged area at the expense of a negligibly shortened canopy.

When summer had passed I thought to wait until spring to move to an airfield while, on the drawing board, I continued to painstakingly record what I had built.

My greatest concern was to find a welcoming airfield; I was rejected by Hamble, Old Sarum and Netheravon. At Thruxton there were ugly rumours afoot and it was no longer the Thruxton I had known. True, familiar faces remained but, as with the Hampshire Aeroplane Club, airfield ownership had changed and James Doran-Webb had been deposed. Furthermore the perimeter taxyway had been turned into a full-blooded motor-racing circuit imprisoned by wire mesh; safety trenches scarred the earth, spectator stands spoiled the view, the scream of engines rent the air and gone was the tranquility of its isolation which had unfailingly called to mind the evocative opening sequences of 'Twelve O'Clock High.'

'. . . one of Bill Gough's lorries pulled up . . .' (Ken Worral).

The recorded voice of R. J. Mitchell provided a mid-January tonic at a thought-provoking lecture given by Jeffrey Quill who told of the Spitfire's continual wartime problems of longitudinal stability, 'We were always on a knife-edge.' Their final resolution appeared to lie in greatly enlarged 'Spiteful' tail surfaces. I motored home in pensive mood.

By mid-March I knew it could only be friendly Thruxton. On the Sunday before Easter 1975 one of Bill Gough's lorries pulled up, carefully driven by Ted Tomlinson. Many willing hands lifted the wing and the engineless fuselage over a five foot garden wall and on to the street through my neighbour's sideway. At Thruxton, wing and fuselage were mated and undercarriage assembled so that by evening, for the first time ever, the little Spitfire stood 'on the gear'. Next day I installed the engine and tailplane. During the two week vacation, daily I worked in a tarpaulin-curtained side bay of the large bitterly-cold hangar while outside it sometimes snowed. When motor-racing closed the field for a day, I stayed home and calculated, from a *Sport Aviation* article, whether the aeroplane had sufficient rudder to recover from a spin; in theory it had.

All the while the sense of unease had increased until ugly rumour crystallized into fact; all aeroplanes had to be out of the hangar by the end of April; it was to be rented out for the storage of agricultural chemicals! My predicament was that I had a completely unknown quantity which had to quickly fly out or be thrown out. Could I make it in time? I applied to the PFA's John Walker for an urgent Permit to Fly while working frantic weekends.

On 19 April we ran the engine but could only achieve 1,800 rpm, the oil

Final assembly in the bitterly cold hangar. Dismantled Zlin in background (Ken Worral).

temperature gauge failed to register and the mag switches did not stop the engine. CFI Jim Mellor got me special dispensation for an extra week. I got a pass to get in during the next day's motor racing and I worked feverishly as 160 mph racing cars hurtled past just outside, their cacophony echoing throughout the dark, cavernous hangar. The next Friday, Tony Clark helped with fuel flow tests, I fined-off the propeller to achieve 2,300 rpm and corrected the mag lead fault. On Sunday I had the satisfaction of taxying up to the pumps for nine gallons of fuel. On Wednesday evening, an assorted collection of vehicles gathered to remove the last of the hangar queens while the flyers were picketed in the open behind the pits; no place for a wooden aeroplane. At the weekend the Spitfire stood alone in the vast hangar, surrounded by growing stacks of fertilizer bags; it seemed a happy omen when John Fairey slow-rolled his two-seat Spitfire overhead, returning from some air display.

Next day I took an afternoon off work and sat in the clubhouse, drinking tea with Vivian Bellamy, newly-arrived from Lands End, while the wind gusted to 25 knots. When it finally abated slightly we stood by the runway while Vivian made some fast taxi runs. 'Well it all seems all right,' he shouted above the idling Continental.

So at 7.35 p.m. on 5 May 1975, he took off on a successful 25 minute flight although he made several landing passes before the Spitfire finally settled; we thought known bumps on the runway were the problem. As he taxied in, 'OK. There's nothing wrong with it though it is a little bit nose heavy.' Then he added, 'Your aeroplane does 150 mph.'

Again, John Fairey had generously offered hangarage at his airstrip but, during a worrying three day wait for improved weather, Vivian admitted

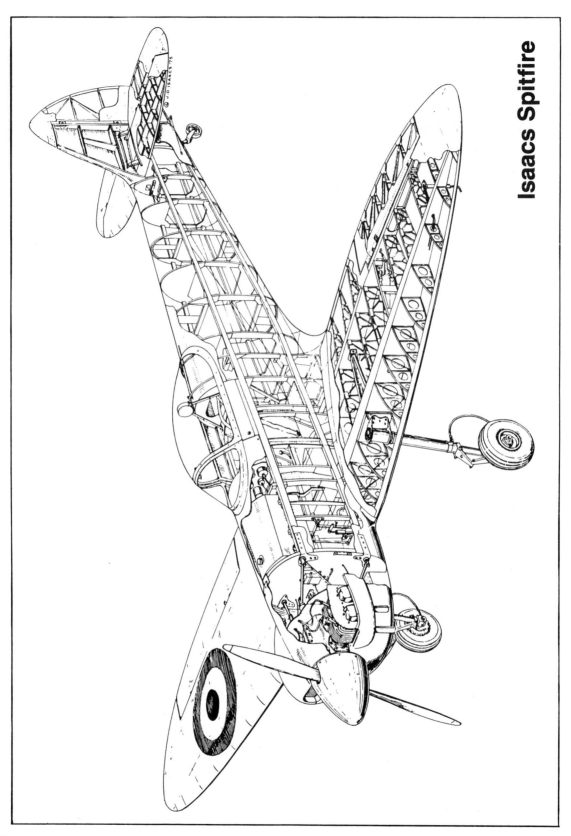

Isaacs Spitfire

The Spitfire airborne at last (A. J. Clark).

that he was not at all sure he could get the Spitfire into the 700 yard airstrip. Meanwhile I checked the tyres, inflated by an enthusiastic helper when we had first arrived, and rather shamefacedly let out 10 psi; I wondered if that accounted for the landing bounces.

On Thursday evening I bribed a fork-lift driver to make a clearway through the stacked chemicals to push the very last aeroplane out of the hangar. It was now or never. After two, much easier, practice landings at Thruxton, to my great relief the aircraft set course for the private strip. It had been a close-run thing!

In good company, at Thruxton, June 1975 (Ken Worral).

Bob Cole flying the repainted (blue/dark blue/white) Spitfire (Geoff Harfield).

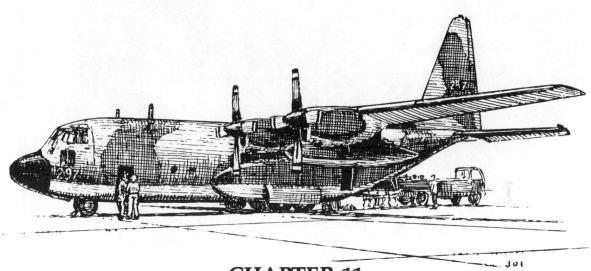

CHAPTER 11

ADVENTURE (1975–1980)

Since provision had been made for varying the tailplane angle, the +2° rigger's incidence was soon reduced to 0° which largely alleviated the reported nose heaviness but, with the departure of Vivian Bellamy imminent, clearly I needed flight test help and was exceedingly fortunate to secure the support of a Royal Air Force test pilot from Boscombe Down. Daily, Flt Lt R. D. (Bob) Cole carried out sickening spins high above Salisbury Plain, perfecting the Hawk Trainer for the RAF for which activities he earned a Queen's Commendation. He had joined the RAF in 1959 and in the course of his career he had been forced to eject from a Lightning on fire at night over the Mediterranean. He was a very fit, good-looking man in his mid-thirties, imbued with that essentially aggressive spirit of a fighter pilot. We all met at the airstrip and, after giving a demonstration flight and a few pointers, Vivian returned to his distant base while Bob went home to think about it. He did not know me and I privately wondered what right I had to expect another man to risk his neck testing my little home-built. I need not have worried; he brought a dedicated professionalism to his task.

The following weekend he returned with knee-pad, test cards and stop-

The PFA Rally, Sywell, July 1975, with Bob Cole on the right. In the centre can be seen the Air Squadron Trophy and Tiger Club Cup (PFA).

watch. That day he flew 2 hours and 10 minutes, finishing with a barrel roll. Orderly testing continued until, at my insistence, Bob borrowed a parachute for the spinning trials. Unfortunately it was a metal-framed affair and it quickly became evident there was no room for it. 'Never mind, I'll do without it,' said Bob. 'I think it will be all right,' he added, for he had already looked at the incipient stage of the spin. I watched anxiously as he completed two eight-turn spins telling myself that the formula in the *Sport Aviation* article had confirmed it would be OK.

It was now apparent that the little aeroplane did indeed 'mirror the flying characteristics of its progenitor'; it possessed fighter-like longitudinal stability although the elevator movement did show it to be positive. It, too, had excessively sensitive and effective elevators, the speed on finals was not easy to control precisely and the float was prolonged. In complete contrast to the earlier biplanes with their built-in drag, this was a clean and slippery aeroplane. Privately, I began to regret the decision to omit flaps.

Until now all landings had been carried out with the canopy closed, so experiments began with the hood slid back at speeds of up to 85 mph: this appeared to help increase drag. At this point in development, practice began on an aerobatic sequence to be presented at the Popular Flying Association's International Rally at Sywell. Here, during two days of glorious sunshine on 4 and 5 July 1975, Bob and the Spitfire became the stars of the show while I was fortunate to be awarded both the Air Squadron Trophy for the best homebuilt aircraft and the newly-awarded Tiger Club Cup for the best original design.

Spitfires on parade at Hamble, 6 March 1976, providing a good size comparison between G-BBJ1 and the real thing (Rodney Poynton).

With 'Ginger' Lacey at Sywell, 1975 (Gordon Leith Smith).

Isaacs Spitfire and Fury prototypes at Lands End, 1977 (J. Woolridge).

I sat on the grass and watched people examining the parked aeroplane when I heard Bob's voice, 'John, have you met Ginger Lacey?' As I scrambled to my feet another voice said, 'Don't bother to get up,' but who would not stand to greet a top scorer from the Battle?

After the Spitfire's moment of glory, Bob gave me a detailed 16 page, pilot assessment, written report on the aircraft and we considered what could be done to improve the situation. The main problem was the lack of drag when landing. The design and incorporation of wing flaps would be a lengthy, complex operation; a more rapid solution seemed to lie in a simple form of underfuselage airbrake which I accordingly schemed on the drawing board. To prove its 'in flight' effect we bolted an aluminium flat plate beneath the cockpit and Bob carefully flew this configuration. As it proved beneficial, I carried out airframe alterations and built in a retractable 'barn door' airbrake which was test flown in September. It caused little trim change on selection, a desired approach speed could be more readily flown and the float was much reduced on landing.

Despite our problems Bob had found the performance of the aircraft impressive. In zero wind, take-off and landing distances had averaged out at 200 yards and 150 yards respectively and 12,000 feet had been reached in 16 minutes 10 seconds. The (innocuous) stall occurred at 47 mph, airbrake down, and 52–54 mph clean. A maximum level speed of 150 mph at 2,700 rpm was confirmed and a cruise of 134 mph at 2,500 rpm. Checks for flutter were made during a 200 mph dive. The roll rate was 90 degrees per second. Height is energy and Bob would scorn any non-aerobatic end to a sortie by saying, 'What a waste of $\frac{1}{2}MV^2$.'

While even the experts were finding it difficult to control approach speeds, I had been reluctant to risk the aircraft or my neck, but with the improvements I prepared myself for solo by flying the Chipmunk from the back seat, the blind area of Peter's broad shoulders ahead simulating the view from the Spitfire, cut off about 20 degrees either side of the nose because of the engine cowlings. At Thruxton I tried a few fast taxi runs in the tiny aeroplane but it was much easier to keep straight on an accelerating take-off so I flew. The exhilarating experience was like nothing I had known before; the aeroplane was so delightfully responsive. Not happy with my first curved approach over the clutter of man-made hazards of wire fence, race bridge and pits, I chose to go round again and I left the airbrake out and the canopy open; once the wheels touched the cut grass swath beside the old runway the Spitfire stayed down. Two more Chipmunk pilots had a turn.

On 6 March 1976, we were privileged to take part in the proceedings of the Mitchell Memorial Symposium, brilliantly organised by the Southampton branch of the Royal Aeronautical Society at the University of Southampton, to celebrate the 40th Anniversary of the Spitfire. In the middle of a full day of presentations by the legendary names associated with that emotive aeroplane – designers, production engineers and pilots, all participants were taken to Hamble airfield where Bob Cole demonstrated G-

BBJI in spirited fashion in company with her forbears: it was a day to treasure ever after.

Back at the airstrip, Bob systematically set about a series of separate flights with varying lengths, sizes and positions of pieces of flex taped to the port elevator trailing edge, the results of which confirmed that the aircraft had normal longitudinal stability. To further improve handling, I changed the tailplane riggers' incidence from zero to −1 degree. Finally, in June '76, Air Commodore G. J. Christopher Paul flew the aeroplane and a Full Permit-to-Fly was approved by the PFA. Work which I had begun on a stick spring-loading device and on a new, larger elevator was abandoned.

At the Technical College, word of my activities reached some of the students. In the classroom, one, more polite and percipient than most, asked, 'Is that right Sir that you designed and built your own aeroplane?' When I assented he replied, 'Excuse me Sir I don't wish to be rude, but what are you doing here?'

I had never been to America but 14 years of reading *Sport Aviation* insidiously nurtured an interest in visiting EAAs week-long annual convention at Oshkosh, Wisconsin; secretly, I also harboured a bolder plan which I confided to Bob; he thought he knew a way.

In the Service, Bob had flown with Air Marshal W. J. Stacey, CBE, FRAeS, who was known as a forthright character and an enthusiastic pilot. We concocted a good story about 'showing the flag' at the American bicentennial celebrations and waited, more in hope than anticipation. Meanwhile, in April, thinking to replace a broken piston ring in the Spitfire's Continental engine, we found a badly-scored cylinder. Urgently I sought to have this refurbished and to have a Rolls-Royce inlet valve modification incorporated. Only at the end of May was the engine serviceable again.

Bob then received an official letter to say that the Spitfire, he and myself would be flown from RAF Lyneham to Washington, Dulles, aboard a C-130 on 15 July 1976, just six weeks hence. The unbelievable had happened, the American adventure was on.

Earlier, casual, discussions with friends on how to handle the aircraft instantly assumed vital importance. Eventually we worked out a scheme based on complete independence. Special equipment was to be used, first to lift the fuselage off the wing after which it was to act as support cradling for transport purposes.

A wooden rectangular frame made of four inch by two inch timber was to be laid on the ground beneath the aeroplane. To each end of this would be attached a removable goalpost straddling the fuselage. Two shaped wooden formers were to fit under the fuselage, one at the engine bulkhead, and one at a frame just forward of the horizontal tail. A lightweight 'Haltrac' hoist was to be slung from each goalpost to lift the fuselage, on its formers, vertically off the wing. The wing, complete with undercarriage, could then be pulled clear sideways to allow the fuselage to be lowered until its two support formers could be bolted to the wooden frame on the ground. The

The Spitfire dismantled, on its transport cradles at RAF Lyneham, July 1976 (Rodney Poynton).

frame carried a substantial location, fitting into the front spar slot beneath the fuselage, to prevent fore and aft movement. The fuselage on its frame would then be ready for transporting.

Meanwhile, the two goalposts, now removed, were to be laid flat on the ground and the open ends of their 'U' form bolted together, in conjunction with a central wooden box, to form a rectangular frame to support the wing, leading edge down, the centre portion of the front spar being clamped on to the box. Light, plywood, leading edge tip steadies bolted to the goalpost crossbeams would complete the wing transport cradle.

To my intense relief Leslie Broomfield, typically, undertook to make the equipment for I had enough to do. Taking my hurriedly-prepared drawings of the transport cradles, I made the first of several 130 mile round trips to Lyneham to confer with the RAF cargo specialists. From home, urgent letters were written to HM Customs and Excise, the Department of Trade for an export licence, the Federal Aviation Administration for permission to operate a foreign aircraft in the USA, the aircraft insurance company, the accommodation office at Oshkosh University, the PFA, the bank, a car rental company. I had written a series of articles on the Spitfire for *Sport Aviation* and Editor Jack Cox had been informed of my plan; he suggested, inter alia, that I write to Mr William H. Meserole, President of EAA's Chapter 4. In addition, I had to decide what to take in the way of tools, ground equipment and spare nuts and bolts to English thread standards; I collected a spare propeller and tyre generously loaned by Doug Bianchi.

So the mad rush continued and, during that record hot summer, Leslie energetically pursued his craft. When the aeroplane had been flown into

Lyneham, the fuel tank drained and flying controls removed, the planned equipment worked beautifully apart from one nasty moment when the fuselage slipped. Then on 14 July Bob and I arrived to nightstop and watch the loading of the Spitfire next morning.

I never knew what lucky circumstances behind the scenes led to my presence on flight 5363 Lyneham to Washington, but on 15 July 1976, I sat beside Bob on a red-webbed folding seat, my back against the starboard fuselage wall of No. 30 Squadron's Hercules, XV297. Nearby, the little Spitfire fuselage flaunted its civilian G-BBJI alongside the disassembled wing – all firmly chained to the floor among the roof-high piles of net-imprisoned boxes; at the rear the closed loading ramp sloped steeply upwards to the tail. The total complement consisted of a five man crew headed by Flt Lt John Todd, supported by other crew members under training, with check pilot, check navigator and five passengers.

A few hours after the 60 tons deadweight lifted from Lyneham's runway, we sat suspended in the sky's blue vault, 26,000 feet over the Atlantic. In the serenity of space the sun's bright glare reflected dazzlingly from the white cloud layer concealing the ocean. Far away on the undefined horizon, distance-diminished puny banks of puffy cumulus bubbled upwards imperceptibly. Drugged by the breathtaking wonder of the panoramic scene, I enjoyed to the full the dreamlike unreality of my unique experience; and how grateful I was for the ear-defender headset so thoughtfully provided by a kind airman and without which long Hercules flights had been described by servicemen as sheer purgatory. Regularly the ubiquitous loadmaster proffered food or drink. Twice, position report cards were passed back, their thin green lines scrawled over the map recording our 300 Knot progress. After seven hours we landed in a Gander drizzle, nightstopped and, following a four and a quarter hour flight, touched down at Dulles International Airport where we taxied to Page Airways hard standing. As I stepped down from the air-conditioned hull into the scorching sunshine, on a distant runway an Air France Concorde thundered into the air.

A stocky, dark-haired, friendly man (perhaps in his mid-forties) stood waiting. I had never met William H. Meserole and only corresponded the previous month when he had immediately offered the hospitality of his home to myself, Bob and his wife Ann, due to follow by scheduled airline; such was the generosity of his international friendship. Bill was a patent attorney and he lived at Rockville, some 25 miles from Dulles, where we soon arrived to meet our kindly hostess, Bernie, the family and Bill's Skybolt project.

That evening I told Bill of our plans. They had seemed sound to me but the first was quickly brushed aside. 'It will be horrendously expensive to hire a car,' he said. 'You can use one of mine.' It being a weekend, on each of the next two days Bill drove us to Dulles where three pairs of hands quickly had the wing back in place and the aircraft 'on the gear' before we broke off for social visits. On Sunday, a 1½ hour drive took us to Bill's playground, the magically (Indian) named Nanjemoy. The resident owner, 'Big Al' Moran, was engaged in building another hangar aided by volunteers; we pitched in.

As the afternoon wore on and the gathering increased I began to realise that these were no strangers to me in a distant foreign land for I recalled their faces staring at me from the pages of *Sport Aviation* – big jovial George Economos, the two trim girls, Joan Moran and Ann Matthesius; all had flown a Breezy to Oshkosh. The airstrip appeared to be sited in the midst of virgin forest and was screened from the nearby road, its existence only revealed by tell-tale clouds of sandy, hot-summer dust which arose in a propeller's slipstream. I roamed to explore this new wonderland, with watchful eye for I had seen in the clubhouse the photograph of a huge snake found in this Eden. That evening, seated at a bench on the concrete pad destined to become the floor of the new hangar, we enjoyed a barbecue meal prepared by the ladies and I felt serenely content. Before we left, 'Big Al' offered to let me keep the Spitfire there until ready to leave for the Convention.

Next morning, Bob Cole and I worked on the Spitfire amongst shining executive 'airplanes' in Dick Dean's spotless Page hangar. By afternoon despite a slight leak problem with the fuel tank we were almost ready. Our host had organised everything. Tuesday saw us in a Washington office to obtain an American Airman's licence apiece; from there United Airlines pilot, Ted Wilkinson, drove us to Maryland airport and then flew us to Dulles in his radio-equipped Cessna 180. When we had reinstalled the fuel tank in the Spitfire, Bob Cole positioned himself behind and to port of the Cessna at the end of the runway to await clearance via Ted's radio. Bob stayed tucked in close on take-off and the tower commented 'Say is that little guy tied to you? What is it anyway?'

We winged our way over woodlands and watched Bob happily aerobatting before we landed at Nanjemoy, hangared the Spitfire and all flew back to pleasant Maryland Airport.

We had crossed the Atlantic, as opportunity allowed, with time in hand to enjoy American hospitality and visit the reconstituted National Air and Space Museum. On our second Sunday we were flown to Nanjemoy where Bob demonstrated the Spitfire. Soon, George Economos appeared overhead in a Breezy and he allowed Ted Wilkinson to give us all rides; it was an extraordinary experience. The aircraft was akin to a Dagling glider. The pilot sat on the nose, the passenger immediately behind but raised to look over his head. The uncovered fuselage was simply a built-up steel tube beam on which the tandem seats were placed; behind them the high strut-braced wing mounted a pusher engine; therefore the 'crew' were fully exposed to the elements but not to propwash. On take-off all passengers were seen to clutch the seat bottom until confidence came. When we had climbed from the clearing in the woods Ted eased back the throttle to talk to me.

At Bill's home I now abandoned the other plans made in England. I had thought to launch Bob in the short-range, non-radio Spitfire and follow him by road, calling in at refuelling airfields to confirm his well-being. But with about 860 road miles to Oshkosh I was advised to travel on the turnpikes with their limited exits besides, it was said, I would never find the remote airstrips. Bob was urged to fly totally independently but both parties would set off on the same day, a Thursday.

Early on that morning I drove Bob to Nanjemoy in Bill's Subaru. When the Spitfire had disappeared into the mist I headed back home but missed a turn on the Beltway and lost myself in down town Washington. Then, in late afternoon, Bill set out in his Volvo with Bernie, Bob's wife Ann and myself. The icebox was vital; it seems that no American would contemplate such a journey without this huge container loaded with coke, lemonade and beer cans awash in a sea of ice. Apart from drinks on wheels, additional 'limey' entertainment came from the CB radio reports which pinpointed the position of 'smokey bears' (police patrol cars) along the route. Late that night, from a motel we phoned a prearranged number and learnt that Bob and the Spitfire were safely down somewhere in the Chicago area.

We swung off the highway at Oshkosh and caught our first glimpse of the hundreds upon hundreds of aeroplanes which already bespattered a vast area of the huge Wittman Field. Within a few minutes I had shown my Lifetime membership card, paid my dues and, to my great relief, quickly spotted the Spitfire: we had come to Mecca.

For a moment I was almost overwhelmed by emotion. Here I was on my first-ever visit to both the USA and the EAA Convention AND with my own aeroplane right on the field, the first visiting homebuilt from Europe. In that treasured moment I thought of all the many people who had helped along the way on both sides of the ocean and I wished that those friends back in England could have been there to share my pride.

As I wandered in those first hours to orientate myself in the crowded complex, I came upon Paul Poberezny in his open-topped VW, Red 1, and was greeted effusively. While we chatted, a stranger came and spoke with him, after which Paul said, 'Do you know who that was?' When I was told my mind flashed back thirty years to that October afternoon when I soloed the little Taylorcraft Plus D; now, C. G. Taylor was still designing new aircraft.

He was only one of so many fine folk I encountered during that nine day 24th Annual Convention. From the Interview Circle these English accents were relayed round the field with those of Harold Best-Devereux and, at the Women's Forum, Jayne Schiek also enticed me on stage. Daily, Bob Cole showed off the Spitfire; he inverted it over Lake Winnebago, flew it for the official film photographer and climbed to 15,000 feet for fun. For a week I trod the length and breadth of the Field, gazing upon antiques, homebuilts, microlights, warbirds and a big husky biplane, its impressive Allison turbo-prop recalling Vivian Bellamy's courageous pioneer work with the little Rover gas turbine 16 years before.

At home I had found it a salutary experience to hover near the parked aeroplane and just listen, so at the Spitfire focal point I was privileged to meet many of the ordinary, unknown EAA members who form the backbone of the movement. Allied to complimentary comment, questions ranged from 'How'd ya get it here?' to 'My gosh, what kind of gas tank has that thing got?' One apparent farmer merely stared and mustered a blunt, 'Well I'll be damned.'

The Oshkosh experience has been so well-covered elsewhere that I will not dwell on it. At 7 o'clock on a Saturday morning I swung the Spitfire's propeller and Bob began the long haul east. The airfield seemed quiet now and the numbers thinned as I walked across the litterfree grass for the last time, started the borrowed Matador, collected Bob's wife and aimed for Washington; my host had already returned and as a matter of mutual convenience we were to ferry home another man's car. A week later, having dismantled the Spitfire again at Dulles to await space in a Hercules, Bob and I flew home to Brize Norton in a white-topped Royal Air Force VC10 at 37,000 feet and Mach .84 and flown by a Canadian pilot. My aeroplane followed in October and was reassembled at Lyneham. Bob Cole had had his personal adventures in the States but when he flew into the home airstrip on the very last leg of the mission he so nearly slid into the hedge landing on wet grass; he had done me proud and left me heavily indebted.

The success of our venture came from the support of so many and the Meserole family and EAA's Chapter 4 in particular will never be forgotten and, as I later wrote in *Sport Aviation*, '. . . we only met the good guys.' To my eternal regret, although I corresponded, I never met my great benefactor, Air Chief Marshal Sir John Stacey, before he died a few years later at the age of 56.

One June evening the following year, we pulled out the Spitfire and I took off along the 90 foot wide grass strip between growing crops. The tail came up, at around 65 mph, the speed increased smartly and I recalled Bob's, '90 mph gives the best compromise between forward view and rate of climb at low level.' At circuit height I watched the ASI hovering at 130 mph and marvelled at the luxury of such speed; craning round in the cockpit I caught sight of the Chipmunk quite unable to keep up. Turning towards the familiar white-scar landmarks of the Somborne Lime quarry, I noted the 12 gaily-coloured hot-air balloons, a mile or two to the north, still suspended motionless in the still air. After orbiting a while I throttled back the engine, reached up to unlock the canopy, twisted sideways to pull it past my shoulders and began a continuous gentle turn to keep the runway in view. Carefully I leaned down to lift the short handle out of its slot on the starboard side, push it forward and lock it down again; the little aeroplane instantly responded, touchily, to the inevitable slight stick movement as the airbrake was extended. The strip of grass ahead of the port wing slid across towards the nose while my eyes constantly flickered from ASI to altimeter.

Pulling the stick back cut off the view ahead and the 'float' ate into the 700 yards. The port wheel hit the ground, we lurched and I rammed the throttle forward as a wing brushed over the crops; I had muffed it. At the precise moment when I realised I was not going to hit the hangar, I saw the

Isaacs Fury II and Spitfire over St Just, Cornwall, 1977 (Ann Fairey).

ASI needle sink to zero; my heart sank with it. A grain had surely entered the underwing pitot head. 'If you are not happy with the strip go to Thruxton,' Peter had said. Wishing to avoid the consequent late evening logistics and distinctly unhappy to have no knowledge of my airspeed, my sole concern now was to get safely down. Telling myself not to panic, on the third attempt I hit a lucky combination of speed and attitude which put me back on the ground. Phew!

At Lands End Aerodrome in Cornwall, there was always aeronautical entertainment. I had just arrived and, totally absorbed, I spread the roll of drawings flat on the table. 'The lady speaks fluent Italian,' Vivian explained. 'So she rang up the company, asked for the managing director who was charming, and these arrived.' They were prints from original factory drawings of Macchi racing seaplanes built for the Schneider Trophy contests of the '20s and they bore the approval signature of the master himself, Mario Castoldi.

Before I left, I drew the blending arcs of the fuselage frame contours on to sheets of ply which, when cut out, became the start of a non-flying scarlet M.39 replica which eventually joined Ray Hilborne's beautiful flying S.5 on the placid waters of Thorpe Park's gravel pit lake. Later, the fascinating exercise of intensive study of the (incomplete) drawings laid bare the mind of their artist designer and the results of my deliberations added accurate drawings to Ron Moulton's *Aeromodeller* Plans Service.

Vivian Bellamy had built up a small business constructing replica

'There had been no drawings for the DH2'.

aircraft. In 1976 his Chief Engineer son, Roderick, had produced a successful Fokker Triplane and an absolutely genuine Sopwith Camel had followed, complete with rotary engine. Built largely by Mike Fenton, it adhered faithfully to the very complete set of drawings supplied by Hawkers dated 1917 and overstamped 'Secret and Confidential'. Vivian flew it at the 1978 Farnborough Air Show when in his 60th year while I, self-consciously clad in a blue jump suit with yellow stripe, assisted as a ground crew member of Leisure Sport's display team on the exhibitor's side of the fence.

There had been no drawings for the DH.2 though its little Pobjoy gave it an air of realism if a poor performance; an hour or two before I arrived on one visit it had fluttered into a field alongside the aerodrome when the engine stopped but was conveniently retrieved, without dismantling, when it was discovered that the wheel track just fitted into a JCB container-bucket. For the Sopwith 1½ Strutter, now at the RAF Museum, Hendon, there was again full drawing coverage.

From such endeavours a real understanding of an aeroplane could be won and what stands out above all else is the sheer integrity of engineering thought shown by the great pioneers, their solution to design problems invariably being the best possible within the constraints of the technical knowledge and materials of their day.

In 1970, memory of the happy spirit of the youthful Supermarine company and the immortality of Mitchell's Spitfire, led a number of ex-employees to form The Supermarine Association with the object of holding an annual reunion. Some years later, the Committee raised money by an appeal for a permanent Southampton memorial to R. J. Mitchell. Meanwhile, I had been invited to act as the Association's Hon. President and when our request for the ceremonial flypast of an RAF Spitfire was denied by the MoD, I was determined that suitable homage should be paid to its creator; I approached the Civil Aviation Authority who, after an initial rebuff, acceded to my plan. On the afternoon of Sunday, 10 September 1978, a modest group assembled in the shadow of the new Itchen bridge, on the site of the former factory in Hazel Road while ex-chief designer Alan Clifton unveiled the large memorial plaque. Moments after his speech, bang on time, Bob Cole appeared in my little Spitfire and rolled those elliptical wings low over the spot which had spawned the first. For me it was a moving moment and I hoped that R. J. would have approved.

After my American adventure, Bill Meserole had boldly essayed the Atlantic crossing in his own Cessna Centurion and in 1979 I was once again invited to his Rockville home and thence to Oshkosh, unencumbered by the Spitfire.

As I planned my second American trip, I received a startling letter inviting me to visit New Zealand where Barry Thompson had built a small Fury, taught himself aerobatics and rapidly accumulated 400 hours on the type; indeed on the day of its first flight I had been roused from my bed at seven one morning by his enthusiastic telephone call while his exuberant letters were always a welcome tonic. I had never met Barry nor had reason to even consider visiting that distant land. With an air of disbelief I re-read the letter, '. . . you have somehow gotta get down here for January 25–6–7–8, 1980. Hock the family jewels John, rob a bank, do somethin' but GET HERE MAN! We will pick you up from the airport, feed you, house you and do yer washin' mate for as long as you care to stay. . .' And another attraction was promised; discreetly I investigated the possibility of getting time off work.

When I arrived at Dulles Bill Meserole had laid my plans. EAA's Chapter 4 held their meetings at America's oldest airport, founded in 1909, and it was at College Park that I was rolled in a veteran 180 hp Globe swift by recently retired Navy Crusader pilot, 'Skip' Staub. At Maryland (Pomonkey) Bill allowed me to land his Centurion before I enjoyed an open cockpit flight in Bob and Dot Haas' Fairchild PT.19 and an even more exposed experience in Breezy as Bill pursued the course of the Potomac. Taken to Shannon Museum in Roger Guest's Citabria I met the legendary Dick Merril. In Washington I was honoured to be taken as a guest to a hotel gathering of the QBs; the Quiet Birds are a select nationwide association of experienced pilots.

The Oshkosh pilgrimage was made in company with Chapter 4 member Bob Crawford who, leaving early one morning, chose to drive his Toyota truck the 900 miles in one long haul so that at three next morning we arrived at the University dormitories where staff worked non-stop allocating rooms. Again, at the greatest air show on earth, I met old friends and new, basked in America's sunshine and rejoiced in the spontaneous friendliness of her people. Not all visitors were indigenous; the international tent provided a meeting place for travellers from afar and there I received a letter from Barry Thompson, personally delivered by New Zealand courier, Max Clear, which presaged delights to come. There, too, I watched blue-headed pins added

A ride in Bob Haas's Fairchild PT-19 (Dorothy Haas).

Gee Bee 'Z' replica and Limey at Oshkosh, 1979 (Harold Best-Devereux).

Russell Woods' Fury over Canterbury Plain, New Zealand (John Byers).

daily to the map of the world until there were 821 of us representing 45 countries; included was that remarkable Australian, Clive Canning, who had flown his homebuilt aeroplane to our PFA rally in England a few years before. While the weeklong spectacle continued, my Toyota chauffeur departed (with ice box) and my host, Bill, flew in so that on the final day the long haul east shrank to four hours by Centurion for five of us.

One night early in January 1980, I stepped aboard Boeing 747 G-BDXD and for the second time embarked on a transcontinental journey to stay with a man I had never met. I had been formally invited to visit New Zealand as honoured guest and speaker at the annual prize giving dinner of the NZ Amateur Aircraft Constructors Association (AACA). British Airways operated a marathon 27 hour, 11,400 mile, direct flight to Auckland with landings at Bombay, Perth and Melbourne. I thus had plenty of time to compare the analogy of my situation with that of Nevil Shute's fictional shy engineer, Keith Stewart, who was dramatically pitchforked into a worldwide adventurous journey from a quiet English suburb; inevitably I identified myself with that 'trustee from the toolroom'.

At Auckland a reception committee of five was waiting. I could not resist personally swinging the propeller to start Barry's Fury on that international airport before climbing into the Cessna 172, piloted by Max Clear, for the half hour formation flight to Te Kowhai (Maori for The Flower). Here in a peaceful rural area of the Waikato basin, eight miles from Hamilton, the 2,500 foot grass strip was owned by Max who was a dairy farmer and builder of a superb Pitts. His airstrip had been chosen as the venue for the 1980 National Fly-In and a small band of workers hastened to improve the facilities. Its two blister hangars were clearly visible from Barry's mile-distant bungalow where two-way radio allowed him to welcome all who flew over. I had been told by a New Zealander at Oshkosh that Barry and his wife Jocelyn had hearts of pure gold and so it proved when, for a month, their home became my headquarters. Both were professionally skilled in the

Pazmany and two Furies near Christchurch, New Zealand (John Byers).

Barry Thompson.

The three Furies and Midget Mustang at Te Kowhai, 1980.

nursing field and, with innate engineering abilities and his zest for the game, Barry was President of the Waikato chapter of the AACA.

After four days assimilation of the local scene, which included a flight to Raglan with Barry, he drove me to Hamilton and thrust an airline ticket into my hand. When I asked about the cost he replied, 'That's none of your business.' The Boeing 737 deposited me at Christchurch in South Island where I was to spend ten days at the home of those charming people, Peter and Lavinia Dyer. Within the hour, Peter had untethered his four-seat Mooney 20 and flown me to the paddock where he kept the splendid little Fury he had built.

In the days that followed, from the cockpit of Simon Spencer-Bower's Tiger Moth, I gazed on Peter's Fury nicely-stationed off our wing tip, met the local fraternity and sampled Bruce Fraser's Pazmany PL.1 homebuilt; then Russell Woods' Fury joined with Peter for a photographic sortie.

One morning, demonstrating remarkable agility for a big man, Peter scrambled out of his seat to sit in the back while I slid across into the left hand command position of his Mooney as we crossed the Canterbury Plains to visit a remote sheep farm set at the foot of a mountain. After carefully surveying the previously unused grass strip, Peter landed uphill; by the time we left, a nor'wester blowing up the valley gave an alarmingly rough ride until we reached 2 or 3,000 feet. At a Wigram airshow I felt as proud as the Red Arrows' commentator when given the microphone to talk the two Furies through their act. Too soon I returned to my Northern HQ by Fokker Friendship. Back at Te Kowhai it rained and rained as frantic preparations continued for the Fly-In three days hence; then the weather relented and the sun shone and a happy phone call from Auckland announced the arrival of Clive and Joan Canning from Australia.

As a local resident, I arrived early at the Fly-In to pound the beat up and down the growing line of aircraft. Peter and Russell had made the long flight North and, with Barry's aeroplane, the promised attraction was fulfilled – three Isaacs Furies lined up side by side, two in the chequerboard livery of

No. 43, one bearing the red bars of No. 1 Squadron. Since the event was held on private property with space limited, it was not widely publicised outside the AACA and therefore took on the proportions of an intimate family affair with a delightful garden party atmosphere. The main flying display on Saturday afternoon featured individual aeroplanes but, for the first time ever, the sight of three Furies in the air together revived boyhood memories of those elegant long-legged interceptors.

It was a hot evening as we walked from Barry's home to the nearby Te Kowhai Memorial Hall, its walls adorned with the names of those who had fought with us in two World Wars. After the dinner, to me fell the honour of presenting the prizes; I shall never forget those 320 people rising to their feet in spontaneous standing ovation when modest Max Clear received the new (Paul Poberezny presented) EAA international award in recognition of his stupendous effort in preparing his property for the Fly-In. Afterwards I was privileged to address the best 'class' I ever had. When I had prepared my speech in England I quickly realised it was not difficult to find nice things to say about New Zealanders for there is no-one like them. In my turn, I was presented with an engraved brass plaque of a RNZAF Hind, 'Nearest thing we could get to a Fury,' said Barry, but I treasure it just the same.

Next day I was particularly pleased to ride in a Volmer Sportsman since I had built the hull frames for Vivian Bellamy's amphibian years before. 'Do you want to look at the scenery or fly it?' said its builder, DC10 Captain, Tony Lynch. With no trimming device it was necessary to pull quite firmly to climb at 65 knots but it would cruise comfortably at 74 knots with a slightly wallowing gait. As the sun dipped below the volcanic hills on that last day the show was over. Fifty-four homebuilt aeroplanes had been registered and about 150 factory types; this in a country of only 3,000,000 people!

Bob Maisey in his KR.1, Te Kowhai, 1980.

New Zealand Furies. Peter Dyer formates on Russell Woods (John Byers).

Next morning I was flown to Taupo to spend a few days with a KR.1 builder. A short, energetic man in his 50s, Bob Maisey was something of a legend in the area and with his wife Jean had earned a reputation for hospitality. He quickly organised my first seaplane experience in a Cessna 206. He was a founder member of the local aero club and, in a Cardinal, we circumnavigated the Lake, flying over a mountainous area at 6,000 feet. Most of the mountains are bush country, so remote and lonely that I could not help thinking we would never be found if we went down there. Here and there, tiny narrow tracks had been hacked out of the bush by deerhunters to serve as airstrips while, at other places, circular clearings denoted patches used by helicopters. When I had swum in the Lake and bathed in the hot pools which Bob managed, he flew me back to Te Kowhai. My happy encounter with him was to prove of importance as will be related.

On my last evening in New Zealand, while enjoying a quiet beer in the shade of Max's hangar, I was plunged into a final adventure when suddenly the cans were thrust aside in a scramble for aeroplanes. I rode in a Cessna 150 with Joe Steel, a spritely sheep farmer in his sixties, Barry took his Fury

Volmer Sportsman ZK-CTY, in New Zealand.

On finals to Te Kowhai in the Volmer Sportsman. Note string on radio mast.

and Max a borrowed Turbulent. We all popped off the ground heading for the hills and the Tasman Sea beyond. Approaching the coast at low level down a valley, we dropped until the hills rose on either side blocking the view. At the beach Joe pulled into a starboard turn round the headland saying, 'It's all right as long as no damn fool is coming the other way.' We shot round the corner to find two Cessnas parked on an otherwise deserted and totally inaccessible beach. A mile further on, Joe chopped the throttle and the wheels dropped on to firm low-tide sand just as Max rolled past with the Fury close behind. Wading out waistdeep to a small reef, Joe and Max soon collected 200 huge mussels while Barry and I paddled in shallower waters of this lonely shore. A few minutes anxiety wondering whether the Fury's Lycoming would start and we were all in the air. For a second or two Max tucked in under our starboard wing so close that he could easily have reached up and touched the aileron. On reflection I was glad I had found time for a preflight lager. At the airstrip food appeared and a fire was lit to cook the harvest from the sea; what a send-off!

Before I left England Barry Thompson had written, 'We will make bloody sure you go back home with enough memories to keep you warm in your retirement! He had kept his promise.

Barry Thompson's personalized notepaper logo.

CHAPTER 12

IN PURSUIT OF ELEGANCE (1980–1985)

In the summer of 1980, I retired from daily toil with three firm intentions; to restart painting in oils, to build another light aeroplane and to write my story. Five years later the tubes of paint remained unopened, aeroplane parts spilled out of a spare bedroom and sheets of manuscript littered the lounge. Again I had been distracted.

As a scale representation of the real thing, I had long been dissatisfied with the 7/10 scale Fury. I felt I could do better and was keen to have a second go so I had begun to collect every scrap of information I could find on the Hawker Fury of 1931.

In 1978, at Tangmere, I had met the enthusiastic Rodi Morgan who, planning to build a full size machine, possessed a very large pile of manufacturing drawings which he loaned me. I obtained a copy of the official Air Publication *AP1419 Volume I, The Fury Aeroplane*. From the USA I bought a set of Peter Westburg's remarkable arrangement drawings which had appeared in *Air Classics* magazine; from Boscombe Down came a copy of a 1929 Martlesham Heath report on the Hornet, immediate forerunner of the Fury; from the parent company came a valuable photographic record of some uncovered structural components of the aeroplane. Work began on a, slightly enlarged, new design until, while assisting Ray Hilborne with the stressing one day, we found the calculated load in a flying wire to be compressive!

It is a matter of history that five Hawker Furies had been shipped to Canada in 1934 in connection with the Toronto Centennial celebrations. During my second visit to the USA, at the National Air and Space Museum library in Washington I unearthed an absolute gem when, in the archives, I found a 15 page report by two Americans, W. J. Crosswell and E. C. Walton, who had flown to Toronto in July, 1934, rather like friendly spies, specifically to study the aeroplane and talk with pilots and mechanics. Their fairly complete description of the Fury helped me fill in some little titbits of detail while their comments and comparisons with their own 'ships' made riveting reading and clearly they were impressed by its performance: who these gentlemen were I know not but there were 16 names on the circulation list of their report.

At home I became immersed in those 1,300 factory drawings printed from microfilm on to sheets each measuring 24 inch × 18 inch. Alas, there were few assembly drawings, most being single detail parts. That there had been no separate register for each type of aeroplane became quickly apparent; a drawing number for a Tomtit component could be immediately followed by the next allocated to a Fury or a Hart. I sorted the drawings into numerical order and wrote a list of their descriptions which were sprinkled with period names such as Palmer brakes, Huson's compass, Aldis sight, Bigsworth chartboard; the location of some parts was obvious, others totally unknown. Over 150 drawings proved to be for the Nimrod.

While trying to solve this tantalizingly incomplete puzzle, I reflected that for years we had dreamed of finding a real Fury hidden away in some remote corner of the world; it had never happened and almost certainly never would. Yet the idea of building a completely new Fury had seemed out of the question. There were a number of Sopwith Camel replicas around but no-one had ever dared accept the formidable challenge of its more complex descendant; besides, where would you find a liquid cooled Rolls-Royce Kestrel engine? Still pondering, I recalled a roadside sign seen near Rockville in the USA which boldly proclaimed, 'The impossible is often the untried.' As my researches continued, insidiously, lured by the thrill of the chase, the quest for understanding, I became drawn into the vortex.

For the mainplanes, no drawing had come to light which showed the ordinates but all the documentation affirmed that the aerofoil section was RAF 28; when I plotted this shape to full scale and attempted to add the known spar cross sections they were too deep to fit within its contour and it became necessary to slightly enlarge the profile.

Fortunately (for the originals had not survived) I had retained the two rib drawings given to me for the 7/10 scale aeroplane 20 years earlier and they became the basis for my recreation for the Fury's 79 full size wooden girder ribs and 58 nose ribs, each with glued and screwed T-section flanges. They had been attached by duralumin angles to high tensile steel spars; the latter posed a major problem.

Each dumb-bell spar had been built of three continuous thin steel strips, the booms being rolled to a 12-sided section and secured to a corrugated web by single lines of cup rivets. To make the booms Hawkers had developed a sturdy rolling mill consisting of a series of (up to ten) paired rollers, electric motor driven; the massive mill existed but not the rollers and the skills, experience and finance to produce them were lacking. Therefore solid, laminated spruce spars were envisaged despite a slight weight penalty. Any deviation from the original produces a domino effect. Wooden ribs could be glued to wooden spars with triangular corner blocks but the design of sheet metal fittings, drag struts and bracing wire plates would all be affected while, to achieve adequate bearing, attachment holes in the spars would need to be drilled large and plugged with dural bushes to accept steel bolts.

At St Just aerodrome in Cornwall, Vivian Bellamy had bartered his Bristol Bulldog mainplanes for the corroded remains of a Nimrod fuselage forepart, long since salvaged from a breaker's yard. Since the Nimrod was a naval contemporary of the Fury, the careful dismantling of this framework proved instructive and demonstrated the durability of stainless steel fittings. A collection of wing fragments arrived, reputed to have been found at the site of a Fury crash; I satisfied myself positively that they were neither Fury nor Nimrod. A two-seat Hector fuselage and wing parts joined the Hawker artefacts while the search for a Kestrel began. At Kingston we sought the support of that aeronautical sage, Bert Tagg, whose knowledge of Hawker manufacturing affairs reached back to the mid-30s.

Part 3 of *AP1419*, *Instructions for Repair of Fury Aeroplane*, included information from which to list and order the variety of steel tube sizes required. Since most of the structure consisted of 50 ton carbon steel tube to British Standard Specification T5, which was no longer available, acceptable alternatives had to be selected.

The fuselage and engine mounting had been built up using circular tubes with squared ends, connected at the joints by flat plates and this presented an early problem. To form the squared ends 'in the field' a hand-cranked mangle-like machine was employed in which the round tube was passed through a pair of rollers which were rotated backwards and forwards while the upper one was gradually screw-pressed down on to the lower, the small vertical movement being accommodated by a sloppy fit between meshing teeth on the two spur gears interconnecting the rollers. I had seen such a machine demonstrated at Tangmere during an Empire Air Day when a schoolboy. It would be a costly thing to make for just one aeroplane.

To some extent the difficulty was sidestepped in two ways; firstly a simplified welded form of construction was employed for the fuselage; secondly, where squaring was essential, local metalworkers skilfully handformed the desired squares with elemental tools.

So, on a remote Cornish aerodrome, in a long narrow workshop which had earlier seen the birth of a scarlet Triplane replica, and which was forever after known as 'the Fokker shop', the Fury fuselage began to take shape. At my 'retirement' bungalow in Hampshire, to which I had moved in 1977, the

Fury centre plane (wooden spars) built by J.O.I. (Peter Tanner).

The cluster joint, centre plane spar root (Peter Tanner).

assembled centre plane occupied a spare bedroom amidst stacks of wing ribs.

The centre plane was structurally asymmetric, the middle one of its three tubular drag struts being offset to port and the smaller bay wire braced; a single diagonal tube across the larger provided for a possible additional fuel tank. Particularly complicated was the ingenious cluster joint at each centre plane rear spar root end. Here two side plates for attaching the outer main plane served as a foundation for fittings securing rear and diagonal centre section struts, rear cross-bracing wires, front and rear landing wires and an aileron cable guide pulley. Detailed drawings of this and other wing joints were lacking but, with guidance from the AP, the design consideration of each proved an absorbing winter entertainment.

The two spars of each main plane were connected by five drag struts, the four bays so formed being cross-braced by streamline wires; evidently the intention was to minimize the small offset, where wires crossed, by reducing their depth without loss of area; it was considered that cheaper, round rods would be acceptable. Drag wires, restraining the wing from being swept back, were opposed by anti-drag wires of different size but there was conflicting evidence as to which were the larger.

A diagram in the AP showed the drag wires to be larger than the anti-drag in the top plane, and the anti-drag larger than the drag in the bottom plane. A careful study of photographs of the uncovered wing structures led me to believe that the reverse was the case and that the AP was wrong. I long pondered the problem until later evidence confirmed my belief. Also, that this wire disposition was brought about by the Fury's very pronounced stagger and the fact that the lift bracing lay in the plane of the top and bottom spars, was corroborated by J. D. Haddon's book on structures, published in 1931; after detailed explanation he wrote, 'On this aeroplane (i.e. an aeroplane of this layout) there would be larger anti-drag wires in the top plane, and larger drag wires in the bottom plane.'

The geometrical complications of stagger, incidence and dihedral as they affected the small Fury have been discussed. Now, I had to make a layout of the real aeroplane in order to design attachments for interplane struts and shackles for the bracing of the biplane wing cellule. Again, a curious anomaly presented itself. The rear lift wire ran from the upper plane rear spar strut anchorage to the lower plane front spar root. A line joining spar nodal points indicated that the shackle should be offset aft of the rear spar to which it was attached, yet close examination of a company photograph showed it to be pointing forward; with some misgiving I stuck to theory.

However, despite our problems, we had our successes for fortune bestowed upon us two inestimable gifts. The first came with access to the Fury Type Records; here was documented a summary of the stressmen's findings which would assist Ray Hilborne, charged with strength investigations. Avidly, I copied page after page of loading figures, each line terminating in a significant reserve factor, witness to the structural integrity of each part. Further, to my joy, accompanying diagrams added vital geometrical detail for which drawings no longer existed; another piece of the jigsaw could be slotted in.

The second came from farther afield. It was known that two Nimrods had been delivered in Denmark in 1933 as pattern aircraft for proposed (but unfulfilled) licence-production. When Vivian's negotiations via the British attaché bore fruit, a large batch of photographic prints of factory assembly drawings were added to our growing store of information; alongside the explanatory technical notes on each drawing had been written their Danish translations. Ultimately, further copies were made to plug gaps in the parent company's records.

Drawings of the Danish naval Nimrod showed both main planes to have a three degree sweepback and, despite a myriad differences to the Fury, the similarly heavily-staggered wing arrangement also specified larger anti-drag

A temporary rig. Note wing structure.

The 'New Zealand' Kestrel installed in the Fury, September 1984 (Bryan Earl).

wires in the top plane. The enigma of the Fury ailerons had exercised my mind for years and the arrival of detailed Nimrod aileron assembly drawings at last brought those essential clues I needed to undertake their design and construction.

So absorbing had become the self-imposed task, so familiar the Fury drawings each with its creator's name appended and many countersigned, S. Camm, that I felt I could have easily slid on to a vacant stool and taken my place naturally in the august company of those designers of 50 years ago. Among about two dozen names appeared that of R. McIntyre so when I learned that he had been section leader responsible for the type I was delighted to hear he was alive and well in his native Scotland. I enjoyed some correspondence with him during which, with humour, he related some fascinating inside stories of the Fury, S. Camm, George Bulman and other aeroplanes.

All the while, museums were being scoured in the constant quest for a 12 cylinder 60° Vee Kestrel; some had been sectioned for display, many were in poor shape, others incomplete. An unusable example was temporarily installed in the fuselage to progress the construction of engine bearers and cowlings. The search spread worldwide; high hopes centred on Africa for our SAAF allies had operated Furies against the Italians in East Africa during the war. In New Zealand the RNZAF had used Kestrel-powered Hinds so I corresponded with the high speed power boat fraternity who had employed modified engines at Wanganui. Despite all our efforts no suitable engine had come to light and even Rolls-Royce were not optimistic.

Early in 1982, the telephone rang and Vivian said, 'What can I do about the engine cowlings? There are no drawings. Do you have any ideas?' It was essential to get the nose of the aeroplane correct as it could make or mar the Fury impression; this was a challenge I had to accept.

The shape of the fireproof bulkhead was believed to be common to both Fury and Nimrod and the Danish drawings gave its contour. Sixty-three inches forward, the Fury front cowl ring was known to be 20¼ inch diameter while six inches aft of this a rear cowl ring was documented. These three known fuselage cross sections were drawn about a common centre line in the head on view and the thrust line position added. By measuring an accurate inboard profile illustration, a reasonable estimate could be made as to where the geared engine's crankshaft centre lay. From this point, a line drawn upwards at 30° to the vertical approximated the location of the cylinder block, itself surmounted by rocker covers known to protrude through clearance holes in the top cowling and concealed by prominent streamline blisters. Smaller blisters midway along the undershield revealed where a structural joint on the engine bearer frame also tried to burst through the tightly-fitted cowlings.

By plotting such known critical data in side, front and plan views, level lines and buttock lines could then be chosen and their shapes lightly sketched, freehand, in all three views until, by constant corrections, in each, a nest of harmoniously-blended contours resulted – the craft of lofting, calling for spatial perception and an eye for line. Using the lofted nose shape, skilled specialists in London rolled and wheeled aluminium sheets to fit on to a 'horse' of templates. In Cornwall, Mike Lamb cut to size the individual panels, stiffened them, beaded the edges and fastened them to the support framework which encaged the scrap Kestrel.

On the original aeroplane an uncovered gravity tank conformed to the fairing line aft of the top cowl panel. The Fury had a fuel capacity of 50 gallons, 27 in the gravity and 23 in the main tank beneath it. To simplify the fuel system and its management it was decided to install in the replica a single 46 gallon tank based on the crumbling sample removed from the salvaged Nimrod forepart; in that naval fighter this had been supplemented by two 16 gallon wing-mounted gravity tanks. By such means was the project hopefully pursued with no engine yet in sight.

It was not all work. Some years earlier Owen Hill had learnt to fly helicopters and one summer evening, from the lawn of his secluded home, in an Enstrom I had my first experience of rotating wings for I had never been an enthusiast despite the undisputed worth of their capabilities. When, the next day, we essayed a return journey to Thruxton I was amused at the thought of two amateurs in their 60s 'wapp-wapping' across a local beauty spot, scene of my low level misdemeanours 25 years before. In Cornwall too there was often opportunity for a Cessna flight and I tried my hand at the Islander twin. At home there was, of course, the Chipmunk.

A fellow member of this group had built himself a small aeroplane of American origin. In the USA, I had met (and liked) the designer who had set out to produce a simple-to-build aircraft regardless of its appearance. It seemed to peform well enough on its VW engine but, with a thick section 'sawn off' wing, the effectiveness of its ailerons left much to be desired. However, it was the visual impact of its stark angular outline which so offended my aesthetic sensibilities that the odium of comparison could not be denied and I recalled the pleasing appearance of the Junior which Mr E. O. Tips had designed specifically to meet the needs of the ULAA in the immediate postwar period. It had not gone into production and, since the Fairey directors had been unwilling to release the drawings, this promising design had been lost.

I never had opportunity to fly it but such were its qualities that, even 36 years later, instructor Vivian Bellamy stated, 'I would have no hesitation in putting anyone with a licence into it on my slop chit.' That was good enough for me. It would be fun to put back the clock and relive a little piece of aviation history. Searching for any surviving drawings I quickly received a hopeful rumour from a correspondent. The report was well-founded and I managed to pursue and purchase what were possibly the only extant drawings, reputedly brought to England by the designer years before. The voice at the other end of the telephone had said, 'I don't think it is an easy aeroplane to build and I believe it has been overengineered.'

Nevertheless, the prototype which had undergone official handling tests at Boscombe Down in November–December 1947 had been described as 'extremely easy and straightforward to fly, with no vices' and the innocuous 'power-off' stall had occurred at an indicated airspeed of 26 knots; all in all it seemed an eminently suitable aerial carriage for a retired gentleman.

The undated drawings, boldly titled Tipsy Junior, showed a Continental engine and an enclosed cockpit, neither feature having figured on the prototypes. Noting many clever design details, I began a close study of the seven photoprinted sheets, ordered some materials and, as opportunity offered, began the leisurely construction of, what I called, the matchstick aeroplane for it was fashioned from, seemingly, the most slender pieces of spruce by comparison with the Fury.

All the while the search for a Kestrel had continued unabated; in Cornwall pieces of dismembered engine lay gathering dust; at my home, correspondence accumulated. Early in a snowy February 1983, Vivian invited me to accompany him to Holland in pursuit of yet another museum Kestrel though, unknown to us, the die was already cast. In a 48 hour dash we crossed from Ramsgate to Dunkirk, drove to the Dutch airbase at Twenthe on the German border and returned via Amsterdam's Aviodome museum; it was all to no avail.

Then I received a letter from Bob Maisey with whom I had stayed at Taupo in New Zealand. With persistent helpfulness he had located a Rolls-Royce Kestrel V engine in a remote motor museum high up in the hills near Puketitiri some 50 miles away; it was said to be complete with magnetos, carburettor and controls and, it was open to offer. The long search was over.

At Hawkers, an excellent inboard profile drawing had survived, dated June 1931 and, curiously, it was titled Sopwith Hawker Fury. Certainly little detail features were indicative of its Sopwith ancestry as, for example, the method of attaching the rudder's lugged hinge bearings to the fin post –

A Fury team. Master craftsman Mike Lamb in black pullover, chief engineer Roderick Bellamy forward of starting handle, and test pilot Vivian on right (Bryan Earl).

Ribstitching the Fury wings (Bryan Earl).

A very happy test pilot – Vivian Bellamy and Fury (Bryan Earl).

just as on the Camel. In other areas, perpetuation of the Wright brothers' bicycle engineering was evident for bicycle spokes secured windscreen framing and clamped pitot tubing to the port interplane strut; bicycle chains and sprockets drove the starting magneto, tailplane-adjusting screw jack and the differential aileron gear. Dealing with the latter, a sprocket salvaged from the Hector served as a pattern and a Fury spindle was designed with guidance from a Nimrod drawing. The Frise ailerons possessed little differential, 26° up and 23° down. As I scrutinized every shred of evidence on such details, the adage of the ageing process was borne in on me with the realisation that I was learning more and more about less and less.

For any schoolboy of my generation, weaned on Capt W. E. Johns' *Popular Flying*, those summer days of 1984 might have represented the ultimate dream. Alone in the house, I rolled out of bed and moved over to the window. Not 30 yards away, the familiar form of a red-cowled, drab brown Sopwith Camel nosed up to a colourfully-camouflaged Fokker D.VII, the one sporting the solid, fluted barrels of twin Vickers, the other a pair of spindly Spandaus. A half-opened door in the decaying hangar behind revealed the shark-like contour of a wingless, black-crossed Albatross flanking a tricolore-ribanded Spad proudly emblazoned 'Vieux Charles'. There was a whiff of history in the air. Beyond the airfield, four miles distant, the puny pinnacle of the Longships' lighthouse rose from sea-washed rocks. I had returned to Cornwall to help further the Fury cause.

The main planes were complete now but uncovered; their biscuit-hued wooden spars and ribs had assumed a varnish-darkened sheen; shiny black drag struts joined the spars, the whole intricate structural pattern held true by crossed bracing wires; one sixteenth inch ply contoured the nose, press-flattened tubing the trailing edge, round tube the bold, curved sweep of the tips.

Precariously, the upper planes were swung into the air and fixed to the centre section, below them the lower planes were attached to the fuselage, then the interplane struts were inserted. Temporary, adjustable steel cables were made up to serve as landing wires though, unwisely as it proved, we did not fit dummy lift wires. When the aeroplane was rigged measurements were taken for the twelve streamline wires required and I carefully calculated the essential manufacturing lengths, allowing for left and right hand threaded ends and forks, prepared a tabulated drawing to go with the order to Bruntons and we resigned ourselves to the six months delivery wait.

The very day we pushed the Fury out for photographs a modest vehicle arrived from Hampshire bearing, beneath plastic wrappings, the professionally-renovated Kestrel; reverently it was brought into the hangar.

The wings were removed again and squeezed into the aeroplane clubhouse where, in the relative comfort of the lounge bar, I spent much of that autumn sewing and stitching aided by Eric, a retired Scot, and, whenever they could be cajoled into service, the more nimble fingers of lady members.

'. . . and fulfill my boyhood dreams' (see Chapter 1, page 16)!

Long-lasting Ceconite was substituted for Irish linen and, when three panels had been joined to span a main plane, the balloon seams were arranged to lie chordwise and the butting edges of the enveloping sheet were handsewn along the trailing edge; 50 years earlier the covering would have been applied on a bias with seams crossing the chord diagonally over four rib bays. Tautening of the latter-day synthetic material was easily accomplished by the passing of a warm household iron over its surface. A Nimrod drawing specified the pitch of the stringing fastening the covering to each rib as 3 inches reduced to 1½ inches in the slipstream wake, its extent defined as the propeller diameter plus one rib bay. Having tied the necessary 1,500 seine knots I went home.

When I returned, the following June, the silver-painted mainplanes, bearing RAF roundels and No. 43 chequerboards, had been reattached to the airframe supported by the temporary landing wires. The first task was to lift the tail on to a tall trestle and jack the wheels clear of the ground. The Fury's long-legged appearance, arising from the need to ensure ground clearance for its 10½ foot diameter wooden Watts propeller, had been accentuated in the air where the load-freed legs extended another six inches. On the replica, initially, oversize wheels and Rapide undercarriage legs raised the upper mainplanes of the levelled aeroplane 10 feet above the ground which enforced a measure of cautious agility on an elderly rigger balanced on makeshift scaffolding and clutching incidence boards and clinometer.

The large amount of stagger on the Fury resulted in an unusual arrangement of interplane bracing. The front lift wire was attached to the fuselage well forward of the bottom plane leading edge and both landing wires met at the root end of the centre plane rear spar; the rear lift wire ran from the front spar of the bottom plane to the rear spar of the top plane. The braced frame so formed by the top rear spar, bottom front spar, the fixed length incidence strut and the rear lift and front landing wire could be regarded as fixed. Henceforth, when adjusting the front and rear struts to obtain the correct incidence, the front portion of the top plane and rear portion of the bottom plane hinged about this frame.

For two weeks we wrestled with the rigging in anticipation of the first running of the resuscitated Kestrel which would follow.

With the streamline bracing wires assembled, the rear lift wires were found to touch the front landing wires where they crossed. With a blinding flash of the obvious I then understood the reason for the, theoretically incorrect, forward-offset rear lift wire shackles on the upper mainplanes. We reversed these fittings in conformity with the wing photograph, unavoidably introduced an offset load and I made mental note to inform Ray Hilborne, while wondering whether Hawkers had trod the same path 50 years ago.

The situation was improved but the starboard wires still fouled. If the upper mainplanes were very slightly askew to the fuselage the fault might be corrected by adjusting the length of one centre plane diagonal strut. Naturally, we did not wish to remove the wings so, with a shortage of ancillary equipment, unorthodox methods had to be employed. Roderick stood on the Kestrel to prevent the centre plane moving; raised on a trestle, Andrew reached up to urge the starboard top plane tip forward; from the elevated bucket of a JCB digger Mark pressed back the port top plane, while I slid home the vital bolt in the aligned holes to secure the adjusted diagonal

The Fury cockpit (Bryan Earl).

'. . . the sight was breathtaking' (Bryan Earl).

strut. The bracing wires were no longer rubbing; the way was clear to finish the rigging.

The single lift wires looked chancy but the type had no history of wing failures. Curiously, I had discovered an addendum (No. 9) in the company's type records to cover the fitting of twin 11/32 BSF front lift wires in place of the single 13/32 BSF size although this certificate of design was dated as late as August 1938.

Alas, sad domestic news suddenly sent me hurrying far away to attend a funeral so when the Kestrel first burst into song I did not hear.

In the weeks that followed my hasty departure the Fury's undercarriage was rebuilt; it is necessarily a complex arrangement, the top ends of both front and rear members being connected to the fuselage by means of universal blocks. Further, the upper end of each of the two fixed-length radius rods, which are cross-braced to form a panel, requires a swivelling attachment to allow axial rotation when movement of the axle ends, in relation to the fuselage, are unequal as when one wheel lands first. For the front legs, Avro 19 shock absorber struts replaced those of the Rapide while wheels and tyres from that revered biplane gave an acceptable scale appearance, despite excessive width, and were stronger than the unbraked large wheels of uncertain origin first fitted.

When Vivian Bellamy's Westward Airways courageously undertook to build a Hawker Fury, it was an advanced project for the type's all-up-weight greatly exceeded that of, say, the 1½ Strutter whose engine power was quadrupled and whose top speed was doubled; compared to the Fury, the World War I creations were light aeroplanes, mere toys. Its construction, on and off, had taken a small team four years to complete with limited resources and, with that lusty Kestrel pushing out well over 600 hp to give a startling power weight ratio of five pounds per horsepower, I was very conscious of my own responsibilities for it had been my privilege to personally build the wings.

In the glamorous age of blondes, Bentleys and biplanes the poetic sweep of the Fury's graceful aerobatics had brought universal acclaim and it carried its own mystical aura of excellence in the Royal Air Force where men like 'Prosser' Hanks, who would so gallantly fight the lost Battle of France, cut their teeth on it. At last, the recreation of a little piece of history would show another generation what it was like and give those who 'cared' a chance to 'understand'. The Fury was always something rather special.

Now was the hour. All evening rain intermittently lashed the 230 mile ribbon of shiny road as, in the headlights, it swept effortlessly beneath the wheels of the pilot's car while a shadow of sadness flickered over our excited thoughts of the morrow. From time to time, the moist muzzles of two black Newfoundland dogs pressed forward from the rear-seat darkness, hopefully seeking another piece of chocolate. At a late hour the BMW slipped into the driveway of a house clinging to the cliff top high above night-shrouded Sennen Cove.

Propitious blue skies ushered in the morn of 11 December 1985 as we drove to the airfield and swung off the road past the lone house, my one-time periodic home. In an instant the sight was breathtaking; the Fury stood on the tarmac, dazzling in its magnificence; highly-polished cowlings glinted in the morning sunshine reflecting its former glory. It had to be 'the day'. I telephoned local club member Bryan, requesting his camera-bearing presence; he arrived and would we like him to get his video camera? He was despatched forthwith to fetch it.

At 2.30 in the afternoon, with Vivian seated high in the cockpit, two crewmen stood, one on each wheel, to lean over the front lift wires and wind the removable cranked starting handles which slowly inched round the enormous propeller until, too well primed, the engine fired and a frightening belch of flame engulfed the exhaust ports before it settled down to warm up. The two or three dozen people on the airfield gathered round

'It had to be ''the day!'' ' (Bryan Earl).

234

'. . . two crewmen stood, one on each wheel . . .' (Bryan Earl).

curiously while, with two men bent over the tailplane, backs to the blast, the throttle was pushed forward until the earth seemed to quiver beneath my feet at the powerful pulse. Throttle back, chocks away and silver wings went bobbing across the grass as the skid ploughed its brown furrow; a turn into wind, an increase in engine sound and, gathering speed, the Fury quickly leapt off the ground and rose steeply, drawn irresistibly upwards by the enormous power unleashed into the fine-pitch propeller. For ten minutes it swooped and soared until the intensely evocative pop and crackle of the closed throttle foretold a landing; slightly high, slightly fast, the first was thrown to the wind, the second, satisfyingly safe on the short downhill runway.

Next morning, a second sortie gathered some performance detail and showed a stall below 60 mph before Atlantic mists swept in for a couple of days. Sadly, the video was sent eastwards by courier. The flights had proved a personal triumph for the pilot; a few years earlier, during a routine flying licence medical, he had heard the chilling words, 'You will never fly again;' but he did, and in the past year alone he had kept his hand in on a Spitfire! All in all, it was a creditable achievement for a man in his 67th year.

But the triumph of the test was tempered by sorrow as our thoughts followed the video east where that gentleman of admirable taste, racing car driver, pilot and patron of the aeronautical arts, he who had commissioned the Fury, the Honourable Patrick Lindsay, lay desperately ill.

The Fury landing after its first flight, 11 December 1985 (Thornley Renfree).

Aviation enthusiasms are international. This is an American-built Isaacs Fury (Robert Hegge).

. . . over 400 hours of in-flight bliss . . . (Barry Thompson).

EPILOGUE

Like books, aviation brought me many of life's greatest joys. In contrast there were moments of fright, not always of my own making; as on the day we were given a lift in a Rapide flown with crass stupidity across Christchurch Bay, invisibly far out from shore, at 20 feet. One of two wartime pilots among the unhappy passengers passed forward a note which lifted the aeroplane 100 feet while the young idiot read it before descending even lower. Perhaps he grew to learn humility, but it has been the sudden demise of real pilots, men like Peter Hillwood and George Hogarth, instantly snatched into oblivion by a combination of weather and engineering problems, which has caused me to speculate on the inexplicable survival of the amateur with but a handful of flying hours. Good training can help, and certainly I had flown with the best, but it is really fickle fortune which constantly determines our affairs.

Good fortune directed me to a more rewarding experience at Supermarine when British Marine Aircraft's plan to build Sikorsky S.42A flying boats under licence at Hamble came to nought. A quirk of fate saved me from obliteration by one of Martin Lutz's bombs in 1940, just as it saved young midshipman Bellamy from death in his burning Spitfire. Good luck got me aboard an RAF Hercules at the right moment. Unforeseen chance drew me to New Zealand whence ties of friendship later produced a Kestrel in the hour of need. By such unpredicatable events are all our lives inextricably entwined.

The convolutions of coincidence seem equally entertaining. After I left King Edward VI school to join Supermarine, the former vacated the site which, much later, became temporary home for a Spitfire when the R. J. Mitchell museum opened there in a Nissen hut. Seven years on, the aeroplane was rehoused in the Hall of Aviation, built, following the demolition of the old Seamen's Mission, on the very spot where, as a lecturer, I had toiled at the chalk face and visualised my Spitfire's span. Again, when I began to build a Tipsy Junior, old PFA records revealed that while I had been the 87th member to join the ULAA, the 88th had been Ernest Oscar Tips.

If the reader has detected a sympathy towards the Royal Air Force it is no accident; that I have been able to tell my tale is evidence of the debt we owe those guardians of the peace and freedom, while those erstwhile tools of their trade, the Fury and the Spitfire, have run like silver threads woven throughout my life.

Lest the reader wonder why these aeroplanes were reduced in scale it is because only by such techniques can a man of modest means represent, for £2–3,000, favourites which full size can cost £250,000.

I have tried to show that aeroplanes are not built in isolation. Help comes in many different forms; specialised skills may be required, a second pair of hands, the loan of tools, advice, moral support and, while Capt W. E. Johns laid the foundations for an understanding of the magic of aviation, Vivian Hampson Bellamy supplied the impetus to put it to the touch.

The homebuilt movement has grown in the 40 years since Ron Clegg's letter to *Flight*, in 1946, led to the formation of the Ultra Light Aircraft Association, which became today's Popular Flying Association with a membership of near 5,000 served by a small full-time staff headed by F. I. V. (John) Walker. In the vast USA the comparable body, the Experimental Aircraft Association, has a six-figure membership.

Aviation's enthusiasms are international and there has always been a universal bond between those who fly. I have told of warm-hearted overseas invitations from total strangers and, in the years since the postwar revival of John Currie's Wot at the Hampshire Aeroplane Club, I have answered hundreds upon hundreds of letters worldwide. Drawings of the little Fury have spread over a score of countries, bringing evocative response from the other side of the world, '. . . I will forever be in your debt for providing me with over 400 hours of sheer in-flight bliss. . .' Others have derived equal enjoyment from construction hours. All have shared the thrill of creative endeavour, the inner fulfilment of the craftsman.

The aeroplanes are changing now, to produce more efficient shapes with higher speeds, and employing new synthetic materials; computer design is replacing many of the old skills of eye, hand and mind. I am glad to have lived and travelled hopefully at a time when traditional materials and methods, properly applied, could produce 'a good honest aeroplane'. My achievement has been modest, my reward great, during a lifelong affaire with the aeroplane.

THE END

INDEX

239